THE GREAT DETECTIVE
PUZZLE BOOK

the text of this book is printed
on 100% recycled paper

THE GREAT DETECTIVE

PUZZLE BOOK

with Other Assorted Brain Teasers

E. R. Emmet

BARNES & NOBLE BOOKS

A DIVISION OF HARPER & ROW, PUBLISHERS
New York, Cambridge, Hagerstown, Philadelphia,
San Francisco, London, Mexico City, São Paulo,
Sydney

FIRST EDITION

ISBN: 0-06-463486-8

LIBRARY OF CONGRESS CATALOG CARD NUMBER: 78-21439

79 80 81 82   10 9 8 7 6 5 4 3 2 1

Contents

(The asterisks indicate how hard the puzzle is, with 5 asterisks for the hardest ones.)

Preface   ix

Part I   Our Factory

1. We Compete. Who Does What? (*)   3
2. How Tall and How Heavy? (**)   4
3. Men-only Mews (***)   5

Part II   Puzzles in Verse

4. The Puzzle of Life (***)   9
5. "Uncle Bungle's Writing Is Not a Pretty
    Sight" (****)   10
6. Crazy Crescent (*****)   11

Part III   Division

7. Some Missing Figures (*)   15
8. Four, Five, Six, Seven (**)   15
9. A Common Incorrectness (*****)   16
10. Letters for Digits (**)   17
11. Some Letters for Digits, Some Digits
    Missing (**)   17

Part IV   The Great Detective

12. Car Trouble (*)   21
13. Why D Was Dumb (*)   22

14. Titus in a Tizzy (*)   23
15. Getting the Professor to the Point (*)   24
16. Let There Be No C (*)   25
17. One and One Make Two (**)   26
18. The Washing Machine That Didn't (**)   27
19. The Professor Versus the Knaves (**)   28
20. Just Seven (**)   29
21. Saved by the Bell (**)   31
22. The Sergeant on His Own (**)   32
23. Blunders from a Blender (**)   34
24. One Too Many Knots? (**)   35
25. Crimes Assorted (***)   36
26. The Puzzle That Was New (***)   38
27. A Disappointed Simple (***)   40
28. Sergeant Simple in Verse (***)   42
29. Good Becomes Better (***)   43
30. The Vertical Tear (***)   45
31. The Professor Goes One Better (****)   46
32. The Worst Was First (****)   47
33. Not Far Enough (****)   49
34. The Last Croak of Doctor Dope (****)   51
35. The Multiplication That Was Worse Than
    Vexation (*****)   54
36. "Four Tribes Are Better Than Three" (**)   56

Part V Letters for Digits

37. Addition: Letters for Digits (Two Numbers) (**)   61
38. Addition: Letters for Digits
    (Four Numbers) (****)   61
39. Addition: Letters for Digits
    (Four of Them Missing) (***)   62
40. Multiplication: Letters for Digits (***)   62

Part VI Soccer

41. Old Method (Four Teams) (*)   65
42. Bungle Blunders Yet Again (**)   65
43. More Goals and More Attractive Soccer (***)   66

44. Uncle Bungle's New Soccer Puzzle
    (Letters for Digits) (**)   66
45. Letters for Digits (Five Teams) (***)   67
46. Soccer and Addition: Letters for Digits (****)   68

Part VII   Cross-Number Puzzles

47. A Cross Number (3 by 3) (**)   71
48. A Cross Number (5 by 5) (***)   72

Part VIII   The Island of Imperfection

49. Ages and Shacks on the Island (****)   75
50. Some Island Soccer (***)   76
51. Hopes and Successes (****)   77

Solutions   79

Preface

This book is inevitably similar in many ways to my previous books of puzzles, but there are some new ideas here that will, I hope, tease the brain in a slightly different way.

There have been many requests for more Great Detective puzzles, and this demand fortunately coincided with greatly increased activity on the part of Professor Knowall, not only in detection, but also in solving puzzles of all kinds, and to some extent, in making up puzzles of his own. This interest is not entirely shared by Sergeant Simple, who, on the whole, has had to follow his master's interest. On one terrible occasion (puzzle number 35), he failed to behave as Sergeants should and, apart from losing his temper, he very nearly lost his job as well. Still, the Professor has increasingly found that these puzzles are just his bottle of wine. There is nothing that he likes more than dealing with a new kind of puzzle whatever it may be and whoever may be involved.

There was, for example, the interesting case of the Island of Imperfection. When a fourth tribe appeared on this wonderful Island, the "I" of the Island stories, who is an elderly and rather an old-fashioned gentleman, was exceedingly distressed because things were not as they were. But the Professor likes things to be not as they were, and there was nothing that pleased him more on one of his visits to the Island than to meet the Jokers (the name of the fourth tribe) and to follow their truth-telling adventures.

The Professor, of course, has been quick to discover and use other new ideas. He was, for example, delighted to be introduced to the new soccer puzzles in which digits are replaced by letters. Puzzles in verse were also a new idea, and although, like so many intelligent mathematicians, "he has not got the fantasy that gives a poet wings," it was an idea that he found difficult to resist. Who knows, before long he may make up some of his own.

Multiplication sums with letters for digits is also a new idea, in my books as a whole and for the Professor and the Sergeant in particular. In fact it was a multiplication sum that led to that unfortunate occasion when the Sergeant lost his cool.

Some of these puzzles are quite hard, but there are also a lot of the Great Detective puzzles and others, which I hope, readers will find fairly easy. Over the years I have made up these puzzles almost entirely for fun (fun to make up and fun on the whole, I hope, to do), but I now tend to think that they can be of considerable educational value. I only hope that my saying that will not put people off; but I have had a certain amount of experience lately in watching the minds and intelligence of the young improve considerably (by almost any test that one can give them) after they become interested in these puzzles. This is partly because those who are really enjoying using their minds may not quite realize the extent to which they are improving them as well; it may seem as though they were very pleasantly riding downhill, but in fact— surprise, surprise—they are really going up!

I am grateful to the London *Sunday Times,* the *New Scientist,* the *Retail Digest,* and the *Surgical News,* where some of these puzzles were previously published. I owe a great deal to my checkers, who between them made many valuable suggestions. Alan Summers checked every puzzle in the book, and David Hall and John Pawson also helped. Accuracy of typing is of the greatest importance in a book of this kind, and I am most grateful to the Winchester Copying Centre and to Joan H. Preston for all the hard work they have done.

But most of all I am indebted to my wife. As the years have passed and she has become more and more interested in these puzzles and better and better at them, she has advised me and helped me in more ways than I could possibly explain. That is, of course, as J. M. Barrie recognized, *What Every Woman Knows,* but astonishingly few men know it. And most women do not tell!

PART I

Our Factory

(1–3)

1. We Compete. Who Does What? (*)

The jobs of my 5 employees, Alf, Bert, Charlie, Duggie, and Ernie, have been changing rather frequently lately, and I am afraid that I have gotten slightly out of touch. It was rather important for me, however, to find out who does what, as they had recently taken a test designed to find out more about their assorted capabilities and it was clearly important for the managing director to know just what had been happening in the past so that he could predict for the future.

The information that I managed to get about their jobs and their places in the test (in which there were no ties) was as follows:

1. Bert was as many places below the Worker as he was above the Door-Knob-Polisher.
2. The Door-Opener was 3 places above Charlie.
3. Alf's place was even, and the Door-Shutter's place was odd.
4. The Bottle-Washer was 2 places above Ernie.

In what order did they come in the test, and what were their jobs?

2. How Tall and How Heavy? (**)

First things first has always been my motto in dealing with the workers in my factory. My public will not, I am sure, be surprised when I tell them of the importance that I have always attached to height and weight. Tall men can after all see over things, and how right was the great Shakespearian character who expressed a preference for having men about him who were fat.

I therefore recently gave my employees (Alf, Bert, Charlie, Duggie, and Ernie) a test or a competition which would, I hope, reveal the facts of these important matters and also encourage them to become taller and heavier.

In these two competitions their places were 1–5, with the tallest and the heaviest at the top. There were no ties.

I am able to reveal the following facts:

1. Bert's places for height and weight are the same even numbers.
2. Duggie's places add up to 7.
3. Charlie is not the tallest of the 5, but he is taller than Ernie though Ernie is heavier than him. The difference between Charlie's and Ernie's places for height is the same as the difference between their places for weight.
4. Alf's place was odd for height and even for weight.

Find the orders of merit for height and weight.

3. Men-only Mews (***)

3/27/80

At the time with which this story deals, Alf, Bert, Charlie, Duggie, and Ernie were living in separate houses in Men-only Mews.

It is useful for the managing director to know the addresses of his staff, but I'm afraid that this information was not very easy to obtain. However, I did manage to get some of them to tell me something:

Duggie said that the number of his house was 3 times the number of Bert's.

Alf said that his number was odd and was 23 more than Ernie's.

Bert said that his number was 9 less than Alf's.

And Charlie said that his number was halfway between Bert's and Duggie's.

Men-only Mews has houses numbered 1–50.

Find the numbers of all their houses.

PART II

Puzzles in Verse

(4–6)

4. The Puzzle of Life (***)

I wish I knew what life was for,
For many years I've wondered.
It is a puzzle; more and more
It seems that someone's blundered.
A puzzle, yes—so *that's* what life's about;
So I will concentrate my tiny mind
On solving just a single one of them:
Two brothers and their ages I must find.
A is twice as old as B
Will be in ten years' time.
And it is true that when B is
Three times what A was when,
Twenty-one years ago, his age was such
That he was still a minor (old or new—
But not aged less than ten),
Then the two digits of his age will add to nine,
                          which will be fine.
If you know who's "he." "I, there's the rub."
Shakespeare, of course, or I might say
That there's the rubber-dubber-dub!
But use your reason, and you will discover
A's age at present and that of his brother.

(One thing I ought to add. They have a clever mum.
Both their birthdays are today; that makes an easy sum.)
          What are A's and B's ages?

5. "Uncle Bungle's Writing Is Not a Pretty Sight" (****)

Shall I guess or shall I say, "I simply cannot read"?
Or just continue asking till all letters are agreed?
In the past I've done some guessing, but I have not got it right.
For Uncle Bungle's writing is not a pretty sight.
So here you'll find a blank or two
Or three or four or maybe more.
Apart from that there's nothing new.
Letters for digits, and the law
Tells us that each one represents,
Yes, the same digit. Is this sense?
And vice, you'll appreciate,
Versa, vice's little mate.

```
        X  A  X  F  K  K  K  K
        K  T  D  H  F  K  K  K
        —  A  —  X  —  K  —  K
        P  T  T  F  D  K  K  K
        _____

        A  R  M  R  —  P  P  P
        ========================
```

Write out the correct addition sum.

10

6. Crazy Crescent (*****)

Oh! Crazy is the Crescent in which my workers dwell.
  I am the boss, and thus I must admit,
Responsible for seeing that with each man all is well,
  Especially that they are always fit.
("Be fit—be fit." As Kipling said, "And once again be fit!"
  That's more important for our staff than having lots of wit!)
But nonetheless wit certainly is needed,
  And what I say must carefully be heeded.
Their numbers in the Crescent? They all shall make a speech.
  So silence, please, and hear what's said by each.
"My number's more than Bert's," said Alf, "by two plus ten."
  Bert talks not of himself, he speaks of other men.
"Charlie's number," so he says, "is just halfway between
  Those of Duggie and of Alf." Then Charlie takes the scene.
"To get my number multiply by three
  Another one. Whose shall it be?
The one of us whose name begins with E."
  "Bert's number's more than mine, I must confess,
By just thirteen," says Dug. "No more, no less."
  Then Ernie speaks and tells us where Alf is,
"Add two to forty-five. That number's his."
  Two of my workers live in the same abode,
Of which there are one hundred in the road.
  One of these statements is simply not true.
He's stupid or a liar. Yes, but who?

  What are the numbers of their houses?

PART III

Division

(7–11)

7. Some Missing Figures (*)

The following long-division sum with most of the figures missing comes out exactly:

```
          2 -
  _ _ ) _ _ _
        _ _
        ‾‾‾
        _ _ _
      3 _ _
      ‾‾‾‾‾
```

Find the correct figures.

8. Four, Five, Six, Seven (**)

"A pattern, that's what I like," said Uncle Bungle. "I can't stand a puzzle that is all over the place. But in this long-division sum the four figures that are given have the great merit of being consecutive." I could see my Uncle's point all right, but unfortunately—and this will not, I think, surprise my readers—his achievements did not come up to his hopes and expectations. I can hardly bear to tell my readers this, but in fact one of those 4 figures was wrong.

The puzzle, as Uncle Bungle gave it to me, looked like this:

```
              - - -
  4 - ) 6 - - -
        - 7
        ‾‾‾
        - - -
      5 - -
      ‾‾‾‾‾
```

Which figure was wrong? Find the correct division sum.

9. A Common Incorrectness

In this long division sum the figures given have this in common—they are all wrong. The sum comes out exactly.

```
                1 6 - 2
        2 9 ) - 0 0 - - 8
                8 6
              _____
                2 - -
                1 2 5
              _____
                  3 - -
                  2 4 8
                _____
                    9 6
                    3 5
                    ===
```

Find the correct figures.

10. Letters for Digits (**)

In this division sum each letter stands for a different digit.
Rewrite the sum with the letters replaced by digits.

```
              s  b  p  x
    s p ) b  r  d  x  r  d
          x  q  s
          ─────
             x  t  x
             t  p  t
             ──────
                c  t  r
                b  y  y
                ──────
                   t  t  d
                   t  t  c
                   ──────
                      x
                      ═
```

11. Some Letters for Digits, Some Digits Missing (**)

In the following division most of the digits are missing but some
are replaced by letters. The same letter stands for the same digit
whenever it appears:

```
                 k  −
    k  − ) k  −  −  −
            −  −  −
            ─────
               −  −
               −  −
               ════
```

Find the correct sum.

PART IV

The Great Detective

(12–36)

12. Car Trouble (*)

Professor Knowall likes everything to be just so. When I took him for a ride in my car recently I had a feeling that he would have something to say about the rattling noise that had been going on for some time. We had been moving for several minutes before he actually said anything, but that was long enough for me to be aware that he was fidgeting in his seat and thus competing with the rattling, about which I felt sure we were about to hear.

"I don't wish to appear to be criticizing you in any way, my dear Sergeant Simple," he said, "but has it ever occurred to you that a man who is unable to detect and put right the sources of car rattles is unlikely to be the sort of sergeant that both of us, I am sure, would like him to be? But let us investigate the rattle."

He was of course quite right, and I saw that the only sensible thing to do was to get together and think.

But first the facts. I was sure that the rattling came from 1 of the 2 doors, 1 of the 2 windows, the sliding roof, or the ash tray.

It was of course the Professor's brilliant idea that we should have what is called a controlled experiment. The results were as follows:

When I fixed the left window and the right door the rattle continued.

When I fixed the ash tray and both windows the rattling continued.

When I fixed the right door, the sliding roof, and the ash tray, the rattling stopped.

What can you say about the cause of the rattle?

13. Why D Was Dumb (*)

It is always nice to visit the Island of Imperfection, and when Professor Knowall suggested that we should go there for a short holiday I was, of course, delighted. Although delighted (for I love that Island), I was also quite suspicious.

"But will it be a holiday?" I asked. "You know what happened last time" (the affair of the knitting needle).

"There is such a thing, my dear Sergeant Simple, as the law of chance," said the Professor. "Let us just say that it is exceedingly unlikely that our services will be needed."

For once the Professor was wrong—yes—just wrong. Before we had been on the Island a few days we were much in demand.

I had better explain. There were then 3 tribes on the Island: the Pukkas, who always tell the truth; the Wotta-Woppas, who never tell the truth; and the Shilli-Shallas, who make statements that are alternately true and false or false and true.

We had in fact arranged to have a chat with four men whom I shall call A, B, C and D. But shortly before our meeting we heard, that under conditions that made my blood hot and my heart cold (I expect the Professor would say that that was impossible), D's voice was made forever silent. It was even more important now for us to have a talk with the other 3 (1 from each tribe); it seemed certain that 1 of them was guilty of the crime.

They spoke as follows:

A: 1. B did it.
    2. C tells the truth at least sometimes.
B: 1. C is the villain.
    2. A belongs to a less truthful tribe than C does.
C: 1. A is a Wotta-Woppa.
    2. D's age was over 40.

I was of course delighted by the speed at which the Professor solved the problem. We would after all now be able to concentrate on other things and perhaps even have a proper holiday.

Who was the villain? What can you say about D's age? Find the tribes to which A, B, and C belong.

22

14. Titus in a Tizzy (*)

I don't think I have ever told my readers anything about Professor Knowall's subject, what in fact he is a Professor *of*. Still, I would not expect our public to be surprised when I tell them that he is a philosopher who specializes in logic.

"Let us all try, my dear Sergeant Simple," he has so often said to me, "to understand that in the great game of detection there are if's and there are then's, and there are causes and there are effects, but these two couples must not be blended together." (Or did he say they *must be?*)

A good example of his skill in dealing with if's and then's is to be found in the case of Titus's bicycle.

I am told that Titus has many friends, but they do not seem to have been particularly friendly on this occasion. They gave him the following information:

1. Either you don't look behind the coal shed or you won't find your bicycle.
2. If you do fail to find your bicycle, it's because you haven't looked under the dining room table.
3. If you don't find your bicycle, it's because you haven't looked on the front porch.
4. You can't both find your bicycle and not fail to look in the cycle shed.

When Titus came to see the Professor for his advice he was in what could only be described as something of a tizzy. It will not surprise my readers to hear that the great man sorted things out for him.

Where should Titus look for his bicycle?

15. Getting the Professor to the Point (*)

"What we are interested in, my dear Sergeant Simple," Professor Knowall said to me one morning, "is the detection of errors. We must be constantly looking for what is wrong. Sometimes the villain may be deliberately trying to deceive us, to make us think that things are not as they in fact are. Sometimes wicked people make mistakes, and we are more likely to spot them if we have minds that have been trained in looking for errors."

When the Professor starts to talk like that, it may be very hard to stop him, but I thought it would help if I managed to get him to the point.

"For example . . ." I said meekly. And to my delight that brought him straight there—to the point I mean.

"Well," he said, "suppose we look at this very simple addition sum. Someone ('Can it be you?' I thought) has been trying to deceive us. I have reason to believe that all the digits are incorrect, though I am glad to say that the same wrong digit stands for the same correct digit wherever it appears and that the same correct digit is always represented by the same wrong digit." My readers will not be surprised to hear that what the Professor "had reason to believe" was in fact quite right.

Here is the addition sum he produced:

$$\begin{array}{r} 307 \\ 237 \\ \hline 732 \\ \hline\hline \end{array}$$

Rather confusing, I found it, but I think that perhaps just trying to solve it made me a better sergeant.

Find the correct addition sum.

16. Let There Be No C (*)

The fame of Professor Knowall—and perhaps, who knows, his assistant also, your and his humble servant, Sergeant Simple— has been spreading. We have been inundated with requests from all sorts of people to solve a great variety of problems. Many of these, of course, have been trivial and not worthy of the attention of two powerful minds. However, many have been interesting, and I present one to my public now that shows the Professor at work in an exceedingly complicated situation.

I am a great one for sorting out what might be called the "guts" of the situation or the argument. In what follows J, K, L, M, N and p, q, r, s, t and A, B, C, D, E stand for events. The information before us was the following:

   (i) J, K, L, M, N are followed by p, q, r, s, t.
   (ii) J, K, N are followed by s, t.
   (iii) K, L, M are followed by r, s.
   (iv) J, L, M are followed by p, q, s.
   (v) p, r, t are followed by B, C, D.
   (vi) p, q, t are followed by A, D, E.
  (vii) r, s, t are followed by A, C, E.
 (viii) p, q, r, s are followed by A, B, D.
   (ix) q, s, t are followed by B, D, E.

The situations are such that it is possible for single events or for 2 or more events in conjunction to cause subsequent events.

You are faced with a situation in which the events J, K, L, M, N would normally be happening but you have it in your power to prevent any of them. How would you prevent C from happening with the minimum of interference with J, K, L, M, N?

17. One and One Make Two (**)

"Never tell them more than you need," Professor Knowall has so often said. "And pay them the compliment, my dear Sergeant Simple, of supposing that they are capable of putting 1 and 1 together to make 2."

As my readers will know, the Professor, though he does not often have the time to turn his attention to anything other than crime, is very interested in soccer and likes making up and solving soccer puzzles.

His remarks about putting 1 and 1 together to make 2 seemed rather silly to me at first, but I soon realized what he meant when he showed me the puzzle.

It was about 4 soccer teams and gave some information concerning the number of matches played, won, lost, etc. However, of the 24 pieces of information that one might have expected, only 12 were given. One did indeed need to put 1 and 1 together to make 2.

The information given was as follows:

Team	Played	Won	Lost	Drawn	Goals for	Goals against
A			0	1	3	3
B	2	1		1		
C			0		9	6
D					0	4

"That ought not be too hard for you, my dear Sergeant," he said, "but I must also add the information that not more than 7 goals were scored in any match."

I'm afraid it was too hard for me, but I hope that the reader will be able to find out the score in each match.

(Each team is eventually going to play each other once.)

26

18. The Washing Machine That Didn't (**)

"A detective is what I am, my dear Sergeant Simple," Professor Knowall has so often said to me.

"And detection is what I am interested in, even though the facts and objects to which you call my attention may appear to be only trivial and unimportant pawns in the game of life."

When the mystery of the washing machine, therefore, was brought to my notice it seemed reasonable to take the Professor at his word and put the facts before him.

This machine, I'm afraid, was not the washing machine it had been. Errors, inefficiencies, and failure to wash had somehow crept in.

Clearly I had to put the facts before the master. I did not feel, however, that I could reveal the terrible things that this machine had been doing. I therefore concealed the facts under a screen of anonymity.

And so neatly anonymous did I make it that the results looked like this:

D, E is followed by q, r.
B, C, E is followed by q, s, t.
A, C, D is followed by p, t.

I showed this proudly to the Professor, but I am afraid that his reaction was disappointing.

"Can't you ever get things right, Sergeant?" he said.

It is a humble Simple who has to confess to his public that the Professor was once more quite right. There was one mistake in the causes: i.e., in the capital letters, so that to get it right one either has to cross one out or add another one (say, F).

On the assumption that each of the faults is caused by single events and not by 2 or more in conjunction or separately, what can you say about Sergeant Simple's mistake and about the causes of the various defects?

19. The Professor Versus the Knaves (*)

I would not say that Professor Knowall actually invented them, but I think he very nearly did and he has taken to them just as though he had—invented them, I mean.

I refer to the soccer puzzles he has been making up recently, in which letters have been substituted for digits. Those who know him well will be aware of the fact that his love for the game started a long time ago and has been growing with the years. More and more he has been concentrating on soccer puzzles (and other puzzles too) as a way of training young detectives.

"The wicked, my dear Sergeant Simple," he has so often said to me, "are sometimes clever too. To detect their knavish tricks we must do some hard thinking. We must think of it as a game, ourselves against the knaves."

The Professor seemed to be particularly pleased with the latest soccer puzzle he set out before me. "Exercise your mind on this," he said proudly, "and you will become a better sergeant."

The puzzle concerned 3 soccer teams that were eventually going to play each other once. A table has been drawn up giving some details of the number of matches played, won, lost, drawn, etc. Each letter stands for the same digit (from 0 to 9) wherever it appears, and different letters stand for different digits.

Here, for the benefit of young detectives who are interested, is the table:

Team	Played	Won	Lost	Drawn	Goals for	Goals against	Points
A	x				t	t	x
B		x			r	p	t
C	x				r	m	p

(Two points are given for a win, and 1 point to each side in a drawn match.)

Find the score in each match.

20. Just Seven (**)

"Has it ever occurred to you, my dear Sergeant Simple," said Professor Knowall one afternoon, "what a very important number 7 is? There were in fact 7 sages, there were 7 sleepers, and there were 7 wonders of the world."

It did not seem to me that there was much connection between these things unless the 7 sleepers became sages and wise and therefore perhaps 1 (or perhaps more than 1) of the wonders of the world. But I did not think this was a comment that it would be desirable to make, for I could see from the Professor's eyes, and the fact that he was looking at a rather messy piece of paper in front of him, that his mind was rather occupied and that he would be even less interested than he usually is in any little joke of mine.

"Look at this," he said, putting in front of me the messy piece of paper. It seemed to me at first to be not only messy but also unintelligible.

I think he saw from my expression that some explanation was needed, and he went on.

"It is in fact a long-division sum in which the only figure given is 7. The question is, did I make it up like that because 7 is such an important number, or is 7 such an important number because I made it up like that?"

Now that I saw what it was all about I must confess that it made me rather sleepy, but I did not think that could qualify as being one of the wonders of the world. Nevertheless, it was a puzzle that the Professor had made up and I could see that there was nothing for it but for me to do my best to solve it.

What I was asked to do of course was to find the missing digits. I would not like to say how long it took. Nevertheless I must slowly be getting rather better at these things, for after a time, which I will not specify, I produced a solution. In fact, it was not quite right but nearly so.

Here is the puzzle.

```
                    - - - - -
        - - ) - - - - - - - -
             - -
             ———
             - - -
             - -
             ———
                 7 -
                 - -
                 ———
                 - - -
                 - - -
                 ═══
```

What was the correct solution of the Professor's puzzle?

21. Saved by the Bell (**)

"If you are going to be a detective, my dear Sergeant Simple," Professor Knowall said to me one morning, "you must be able to use the mind that nature gave you. You must be able to reason and to see how little sentences like 'If so and so, then something else' work."

"Let us give you a little practice."

I must say that I was not very keen on the test that the Professor was obviously going to give me, for on the whole, I prefer to solve my problems by what I would describe as intelligent guessing. But I saw no way of avoiding the questions that the Professor was obviously going to ask me.

"Let us suppose," he said, "that p is true and that we have to find out whether x, y, and z are true."

A sort of haze passed over my mind as it always did when I heard about x, y, and z, though I did not mind about p so much.

"Apart from the fact that p is true, you are given 3 bits of information.

"The first one is that if x is true, then y is false.

"The second one is that if z is true, then y is true.

"And the third one is that if z is false, then p is false.

"All you have to do, my dear Sergeant, is to discover whether x, y, and z are true or false."

As I expected, the haze was getting hazier, but I felt that it was very important that I should play for time.

"That seems pretty easy," I said. "But have you considered what the situation would be if p were not true?"

And then the miracle happened—the telephone bell rang and the Professor was called out to deal with something that was rather more important than whether x, y, and z were true or false.

What can you say about the truth or falsehood of x, y, and z if p is true? Also, what can you say about them if you are told that p is false?

22. The Sergeant on His Own (**)

"I want you, my dear Sergeant," said Professor Knowall to me one day, "to become better and better at using the intelligence which God so kindly gave you."

I thought it was exceedingly nice of him to say that. Nothing the reader will have noticed, about the *little* intelligence, and I felt determined to show him that I really had quite a lot that could be used, not only for finding criminals, but also for solving puzzles. I would make it plain for all to see that he was right to leave out "little."

I have always been rather keen on long division, and I particularly liked the puzzles the Professor had made up with letters substituted for digits. They seem to me to have the great advantage that a powerful mind is not really required (though, of course, they need rather more than a little one).

Over the years I had learned a great many tricks from the Professor, and I was determined to use them all in this test of my ability. This was going to be a puzzle to end all puzzles. When I had finished I showed it to the Professor. He looked at it carefully and then he said, "This is a puzzle to end all puzzles. Once you start getting letters wrong and give no information that you have done so, the whole business of making up puzzles comes to a grinding halt. One of the letters is wrong."

I don't quite know why, but I think that the Professor was determined to be kind to me. Perhaps, after all, I was not such a bad sergeant as sergeants go, and he might not find it easy to replace me if I went.

"The great thing to do when you make a mistake," he said, "is to try, as it were, and turn things upside down and make the best of it. This shall now be a rather subtle puzzle, with one of the letters incorrect. And in this way, my good Sergeant, good comes out of evil. Mistakes are turned to our advantage, and out of error a new and better puzzle is born."

Well, I must say this really was very kind of him, and I have great pleasure in putting my puzzle before the public.

I think everybody knows the rules about this except for the one letter that is wrong (on one of the occasions when it appears if it appears more than once). Letters stand for digits, and the same letter stands for the same digit.

```
              a  d  c  d
      p d ) m  m  c  f  d  d
            e  i
           ─────
            p  e  f
            p  c  m
              ─────
              m  d  d
              m  d  c
                 ─────
                 h  d
                 p  d
                ─────
                 m  f
                ═════
```

You are asked to find which letter is wrong (and what it should be) and to write out the division sum with letters replaced by digits.

23. Blunders from a Blender (**)

Some people might say that the latest problem on which the great Professor Knowall has been engaged is something too insignificant for his powerful mind. Still, I think it is important that it be recorded for posterity. It shows how swiftly the Professor moved in discovering a logical mistake. Even though the mistake in this case was one of my own making, I am prepared to disclose it for the sake of professors and sergeants yet unborn.

"You must be prepared, Simple," the Professor has so often said, "to show what a fool you are so that others may see the light."

It was all about a little matter of an improperly behaving blender belonging to a lady friend of mine. As a good sergeant should, I put the facts neatly down on paper for the convenience of the Professor and of anyone else who might be interested. In doing this I was using an old wrinkle of my mentor.

"Simplify," he always said. "The correct word is a step toward smaller sentences." (I never quite knew whether this was a hint to the detective or advice to the criminal.)

Anyway, I did as the Professor suggested and put the evidence that I had neatly on paper. It looked like this:

A, C, D are followed by p, r.
A, B, D, E are followed by q, r.
A, E are followed by q, s.

When I showed this to the Professor, however, it did not take him long to discover that I had made a mistake.

"Wrong again, Sergeant Simple," he said. "You have left out one small letter."

On the assumption that each of the faults in the blender is caused by a single event and not by 2 or more in conjunction, find the letter that was left out and the cause of p, q, r, and s.

24. One Too Many Knots? (**)

It is very sad to have to say and, indeed, to think this, but there seems to be no escaping the fact that the thief must have been one of those 5 charming ladies. I have written down very carefully, as I usually do, just what happened and just what was said on that morning.

Professor Knowall and I were hard at work solving crime, making suggestions to the police, and trying hard to assist in the making of a better world. It was therefore rather a shock for us to realize that charm had not been sufficient to prevent a bit of thieving.

Under conditions that made it clear that one of them was not the lady we thought she was, either Anna, Belinda, Cecilia, Dora, or Eve had stolen the Professor's wallet.

We managed to get 4 of them to make statements as follows:

Cecilia said that it was not Belinda or Eve.
Belinda said that Eve said that it was not Anna or Dora.
Dora said that it was not Anna or Cecilia.
Anna said that it was not Belinda, Dora, or Eve.

"It seems to me," I said, "a pretty knotty problem."

The Professor laughed at that. "You might say," he said, "that (and I have it on the best authority that this is so) there are one too many knots. But, my dear Sergeant Simple, there are knots and knots."

I saw no reason for his mirth. It so happens that knots are one of the very few things about which I know rather more than the Professor does.

"There are knots and knots," seemed to me to be a very silly statement. Of course there are knots and knots. Everybody knows that. And to say it did not in the least help us to solve the problem.

But as a matter of fact it did, and very soon the Professor advised the police to make an arrest.

Who was arrested and why?

25. Crimes Assorted (***)

When Professor Knowall and I came to the Island of Imperfection we had hoped for a long quiet holiday. But it was not to be. Our arrival seemed to have triggered off a whole series of misdemeanors, and our hope of sitting in the sun, perhaps under a palm tree, and having a few gorgeous lady Wotta-Woppas fanning our fevered brows did not look like becoming more than a hope.

There are 3 tribes on the island: the Pukkas, who always tell the truth; the Wotta-Woppas, who never tell the truth; and the Shilli-Shallas, who make statements which are alternately true and false or false and true.

The police on the island, who are all good Pukkas and true, had told us that on the day before there had been 3 separate actions against the laws of the island: one of them was a case of dangerous drinking, one of provoked assault, and one of bobbery (there has been a lot of this on the island recently; it means robbing a bobby).

Since we knew that the police were all Pukkas, there seemed to me to be a lot to be said for letting them do the investigations and then we could use our minds to interpret and come to the conclusions on whatever they found. But the Professor would not have this.

"Duty before palm trees and gorgeous Wotta-Woppas, my dear Sergeant Simple," he said. "A detective must detect, and the sun seems to have sharpened up my wits and my enthusiasm."

I don't quite know how he did it, but very shortly the Professor had in front of us 3 inhabitants of the island who had been persuaded or perhaps forced to make statements. These statements of course conformed to their tribal customs, and fortunately we knew that there was 1 man from each tribe. It seemed pretty clear from the investigations that we had made that there was no reason why all the crimes could not all have been committed by the same person.

The 3 inhabitants of the island, whom I shall call A, B, and C, spoke as follows:

A: 1. C was the dangerous drinker.
   2. I am not the most truthful of the 3 of us.
   3. When asked whether C was a Pukka, B said "Yes."
B: 1. A was the man who was guilty of provoked assault.
   2. A is a Wotta-Woppa.
   3. C was guilty of bobbery.
C: 1. One of us was guilty of more than 1 offence.
   2. B was not guilty of provoked assault.
   3. A was guilty of dangerous drinking.

It will not surprise my readers to know that the Professor did not take long to arrive at his conclusion.

What can you say about who was guilty of the 3 offences?

26. The Puzzle That Was New (***)

"New shall be the letters," said Professor Knowall one evening with great glee, "and new shall be the name of the puzzle."

My readers will not be surprised to hear that I had not the slightest idea what he was talking about. But if I may be allowed a small pun on what he said, there is nothing new in that.

The Professor, of course, rather likes me not to understand what he is saying. It gives him the chance of explaining things, and there is no one who enjoys that more. There was a time when I would have pretended to understand, but I find it much better now (and more pleasing to him) to confess my ignorance for all (or at least for him) to see.

"I'm afraid," I said, "that I don't quite understand what you are talking about."

" 'Not quite,' my dear Sergeant Simple," he said, "isn't that a bit of an understatement? Why not confess that you haven't the slightest idea?"

"But I really can't blame you," he went on, "for I must confess that if I were in your position I would feel the same."

This was such a startling and unexpected confession that I felt my heart warming toward my boss.

"We are 2 of a kind," he seemed to be saying, "and I am sometimes puzzled too."

Yes, 2 of a kind, that's what we were. With a warm heart and a mind that seemed to be working rather better than usual I listened carefully to his explanation.

It was all about a long-division sum with letters for digits. Right in the middle of the sum could be seen the word "new," and in fact these were the only letters to appear, and my readers will not be surprised to hear that most of the figures were missing. The same letter, of course, as the Professor was careful to explain to me, stands for the same digit wherever it appears, and different letters stand for different digits.

The sum that the Professor put in front of me was as follows:

```
              n  -  -  -
    w  -  ) -  -  -  -  -
           -  -
           ‾‾‾‾‾
              -  -  n
           e  -  w
           ‾‾‾‾‾‾‾
              -  w  -
           w  -  -
           ‾‾‾‾‾‾‾
                 n
                 =
```

I think I must be getting rather better at these things. With a bit of help and encouragement from the Professor, the reader will no doubt be surprised to hear, it wasn't too long before I was able to put in front of him the correct answer (or at least nearly the correct answer).

Write out the complete division sum.

27. A Disappointed Simple (***)

"Cooperation. That's what we should be aiming at," said Professor Knowall one morning. "Two, rather than always, one. The result of that could be a new and better puzzle."

I must say that I was rather surprised by this. It did seem that at last the Professor was prepared to recognize some of the hard work—yes, and hard thinking—that I had been doing over the years.

"It's very nice of you to say so," I said, "and it is kind of you to recognize my work." The Professor looked at me in some astonishment. "I don't know what you are talking about," he said, "I am referring to a new kind of puzzle: Suppose that we had a soccer puzzle with letters for digits and an addition sum with the same letters standing for the same digits; and suppose that each of them was quite impossible without the help of the other. It opens up," said the Professor enthusiastically, "a new range of puzzles for us."

I cannot say that I understood what he was talking about, but it was only too clear that he was not talking about the cooperation for which I had hoped. It was not going to be me and him, but one kind of ruddy puzzle and another (I apologize for my language).

Although, as you will understand, I am now a rather disappointed and angry sergeant, I suppose I must give my readers the puzzle which the Professor put in front of me.

Perhaps I had better remind my readers that in the following soccer table and addition sum, letters have been substituted for digits (from 0 to 9). The same letter stands for the same digit wherever it appears, and different letters stand for different digits. The 4 teams are eventually going to play each other once—or perhaps they have already done so.

(i) Team	Played	Won	Lost	Drawn	Goals for	Goals against	Points
A				y	p	x	h
B	n	h			t		x
C	g				p	h	
D					y	n	

(ii)

$$
\begin{array}{cc}
p & n \\
h & g \\
\hline
t & x \\
\hline
\hline
\end{array}
$$

(Two points are given for a win, and 1 point to each side in a drawn match.)

Find the scores in the soccer matches and write the addition sum out with numbers substituted for letters.

28. Sergeant Simple in Verse (***)

I am Sergeant Simple and I keep the notes and diaries
Of my boss Professor Knowall, magic name;
I do all the donkey work and help in the enquiries,
So the Prof. can close his eyes and use his brain.
  But it is not only crime which occupies the mind.
  For we also follow soccer here and there,
    And I will tell you now of a most important find
    Which made a nonsense problem crystal clear.
This is soccer for a few,
By a method which is new,
Ten and five are points awarded for a win and for a draw,
And a point for every goal that has been scored.
  If you ask what that is for,
  I reply that that's the law
And more goals will be obtained as the reward.
Four teams all played each other, it does not matter when,
A and C got eight points each and B nineteen, and then
One more got fifty-seven. And here's a problem rich,
For one team's points are incorrect. I must not tell you which.
  But Professor Knowall knows and he says this:
"If I give the information that you can discover which,
Why then you will be able so to do."
  The Professor, as we know, is good at many things,
But he has not got the fantasy that gives a poet wings.
Two bits of information that will help in your approach
And you can then the puzzle solve. For when
A match is played at least one goal is scored by both,
But they never scored together more than ten.

Which figure was wrong? And what information can you give
about the score in each match?

29. Good Becomes Better (***)

It is true that when Professor Knowall has his mind on detection
or on solving puzzles he tends to forget all else. Although I don't
like to criticize the great man, the fact that others—especially
me—have souls that can be wounded by criticism has sometimes
escaped his notice. Recently I found him in rather a different
mood. Many villains had been found and many puzzles had been
solved, and he was just putting his feet up and resting.

"You might, my dear Sergeant Simple," he said to me one
evening when he was in such a mood "like to exercise your
mind" (no, he did not say "your little mind")" on solving this
puzzle. I think you will find it quite easy." (No—he did not say
"*even* you.") And he tossed over to me a puzzle that seemed to be
(in fact he said it was) an addition sum with letters for digits.

When I had written it out properly it looked like this:

$$
\begin{array}{ccccccc}
 & R & R & D & B & T & D & P \\
 & R & W & A & D & T & D & P \\
\hline
T & R & W & H & E & M & T & R \\
\end{array}
$$

This I thought was my chance to show that I am not as stupid
as he often says I am, and I sat down at my desk determined that
this time I should be successful.

But time passed and no solution came. In fact, I am bound to
say that it seemed to be impossible. But I still went on trying until
I became aware of the fact that the Professor was standing
behind me looking down.

"My dear Sergeant Simple," and his voice was not quite as kind
as it had been when he was nearly horizontal, "you have made a
mistake. Are you incapable of copying down a few letters? You
have got one of the letters wrong on one of the occasions on
which it appears (if it appears more than once)."

Well, of course, if I had known that, things would have been
quite different. With the help of the work I had already done on
the puzzle, I was, I am proud to say, able to discover the letter
that was wrong and to solve the whole problem. It was quite a

nice problem as he originally set it. (Was it his writing or my reading that was at fault?) But I reckon it became a much better and more interesting problem as it is now.

Which letter was wrong? Write the correct sum with numbers substituted for letters.

30. The Vertical Tear (***)

Professor Knowall is, I'm afraid, a very untidy man, and I was not surprised when I found in the Wagger-Pagger-Bagger (sorry, I mean the wastepaper basket) what appeared to be half a soccer puzzle. I did not think that the Professor meant it to be there for I could not think that he had made a mistake. As my readers will know, he does not make mistakes (except, of course, in throwing things into the Wagger-Pagger-Bagger).

The Professor was not very pleased when I showed him what I had found. He liked to think that his actions and his fingers were as tidy as his mind undoubtedly is. He thanked me rather gruffly and then concentrated on the tattered paper that I had given him, in which all that could be read were the goals against and the points, although the last of those was unfortunately illegible.

"Out of carelessness and untidiness, my dear Sergeant Simple," he said, "a new kind of puzzle can emerge. It has happened right now." He went on with growing enthusiasm. "This is a new and better puzzle than I had envisaged. Well done, Sergeant!" he said, but rather sarcastically, I thought.

"Anyway," he went on, "the great thing is that this puzzle can be solved just as it is, if one bears in mind the fact that 1 figure is wrong, though fortunately it is only 1 out (i.e., 1 more or 1 less than the correct figure)."

The Professor did not attempt to explain or justify the last remark, but I think we must take it to be true. Two points are of course given for a win and 1 point to each side for a draw.

The figures on the tattered piece of paper were as follows:

Goals against	Points
5	3
6	5
0	0
7	?

Each side played at least 1 game, and not more than 7 goals were scored in any match.

Calling the teams A, B, C, and D in that order, find the figure that was wrong and the score in each match.

45

31. The Professor Goes One Better (****)

"Why must we always be solving mysteries, my dear Sergeant Simple," said Professor Knowall to me one evening. "Let us, for a change, ask the questions and get others to answer them."

This was a new idea to me, and I thought we would be in for something original. Nor was I mistaken.

"Let us make up," he said, "a soccer puzzle using the new method, but giving it an even newer twist."

In case my readers do not know about this new method, I had better explain it. In it 10 points are awarded for a win, 5 points for a draw, and 1 point for each goal scored. The new twist that the Professor was proposing was that 1 bonus point should be given for 2 successive goals, 2 bonus points for 3 successive goals, 4 bonus points for 5 successive goals, and so on.

No one will be surprised when I tell them how swiftly the Professor produced the puzzle.

"There shall be 4 teams," he said, rather, I thought, as though he were the Almighty, "and their points shall be A 22, B 9, C 25, and D 8. Two of the matches shall not have been played, and furthermore, in each match, 1 side and 1 side only shall have gotten a bonus. Moreover, each team shall have gotten at least 1 bonus, this bonus shall be more than 2 points in at least 1 match."

"Is that all the information you are going to give me?" I said. "Is there nothing about the goals scored?"

"Yes, yes," he said, looking swiftly at his notes. "Each team will have gotten at least 1 goal in every match, and there was a game in which A scored 4 goals."

My public will not be surprised to hear that this was too much for me, but I hope it will not be too much for them.

What was the score in each match?

32. The Worst Was First (****)

"I have been doing some thinking," said Professor Knowall one afternoon, "and I have come to a very important conclusion."

It did not seem necessary for me to say anything, so I just looked intelligent.

"Are you all right?" said the Professor, looking at me with some alarm. Since that seemed to be what he wanted, I stopped looking intelligent. The alarm left his face, and he went on. "You know, my dear Sergeant Simple, this new method of encouraging goals in soccer matches by awarding 10 points for a win, 5 points for a draw, and 1 point for each goal scored? Well, if 1 team in a competition scores a lot of goals but fails to win a match, it might end up coming top of the league."

It did not seem to me that that was either likely or indeed possible. But I knew that my thoughts on the matter would not be of much interest to the Professor.

"This is something," he went on, "on which one can exercise one's ability to detect. Halloo, hally, oh, gorgeous day. What a puzzle that will be."

I was not quite able to share his enthusiasm, and it was far from being my idea of a gorgeous day. But after all, he is my boss and I must try to follow him with as much enthusiasm as I can muster.

It did not take the Professor long to produce the relevant figures to prove (he hoped) his theory. His puzzle was as follows:

Four teams A, B, C, and D are to play each of the others once. The team that came first lost all its matches. Ten points were awarded for a win, 5 points for a draw, and 1 point for each goal scored, whatever the result of the match.

The results were as follows:

B   45 points
D   43 points
A   39 points
C   34 points

In the matches between A, C, and D not more than 3 goals were scored in any match, and in the matches that B played neither side scored more than 18 goals. Each match that was won was won by a single goal.

Find the score in each match.

33. Not Far Enough (****)

Like many other things, my division is not what it was, especially perhaps, my long division. However, there seemed to be something wrong with the sum (for a sum is what it appeared to be) that Professor Knowall tossed over to me late one winter evening after we had dined and wined as old-fashioned gentlemen should.

"What do you make of this?" he asked. The answer of course was that I made nothing of it; my task was not made any easier by the fact that, although the Professor is always making rude remarks about my writing, I find his pretty illegible too. But I could read enough to know that something was wrong. Just to make a very simple point, twice 39 is not, and never has been, 47.

"It seems to me," I said, "that these figures cannot all be right."

"You have got something there, my dear Sergeant Simple," he said, "but as usual you don't go far enough. You never do. I suggest that you see whether you can solve this problem, for a problem it is, on your own. The hard thinking that is needed will help you in your attempts to be a detective."

I did not think this last remark was very kind, but he went on: "I will just give you the clue that for you to say as you did, that the figures cannot all be right, was the understatement of the year. In fact, they are all wrong."

I felt that after this challenge I had to solve the problem, however long it took—and I would not like to say how long that was.

The figures of the division sum were as follows:

$$
\begin{array}{r}
2\,5\,3\,-\,- \\
3\,9\,)\;\overline{-\,-\,-\,-\,-\,-} \\
4\,7 \\
\overline{} \\
2\,-\,- \\
1\,8\,0 \\
\overline{} \\
5\,-\,- \\
3\,2\,6 \\
\overline{} \\
9\,- \\
5\,1 \\
\overline{} \\
1\,-\,2 \\
-\,4\,4 \\
\overline{\overline{}}
\end{array}
$$

Find all the figures of the correct sum.

34. The Last Croak of Doctor Dope (****)

Professor Knowall and I were enjoying the luxury of a nice cup of coffee in the middle of the morning when suddenly the telephone rang. Somehow it seemed to be especially loud and clear, as though the tidings it had to give us could not be delayed. But not for long. The Professor's left hand went out and his right hand was ready in a flash to jot down the details of the latest mystery. I thought it would probably be a wrong number, but I was wrong. I often am. I could see by the Professor's expression that the bloodhound was on some sort of a trail.

"Was he quite dead?" I heard him ask.

"When was he last seen alive, and when was the corpse discovered?"

In a minute or two he put the receiver down. Having finished my coffee, I was just putting my boots on, ready for the journey we were obviously going to have to make.

"A timetable, my dear Sergeant Simple, quick," he said. Having dealt with his request, I tightened my boot laces, for it looked as though our journey was going to be a long one. But it seemed I was mistaken. "You don't need your boots just yet, my dear Sergeant," said the Professor, "but later on we shall be paying a visit to Criss Cross."

How silly, I thought, can professors become. The village of Criss Cross and its station was only half a mile away along the road. For what possible purpose could one want to look in a timetable to find out how to get there?

But, as usual, I had gotten hold of the wrong end of a few sticks. We were not going anywhere by train; the timetable was to give us information about other people's movements.

In his own good time the Professor explained to me what the situation was. The mangled body of Doctor Dope had been discovered in the waiting room of the station. The Professor, with his fantastic memory, gave me a few details of what was known about the man, especially his habits as a doctor. Apparently, Dope was his name, and dope was what he was keen on, in his professional capacity. In fact, I gather that it had been suggested that his method with his patients was to give them

51

either slow-you-down dope or pep-you-up dope. Not surprisingly, these methods did not meet with the approval of all. Just before his body had been found the station master had heard a terrible croak.

To cut a long story shorter, it seemed that 4 of the doctor's patients were known to be after his blood. Their names were Quick, Racy, Sleepy, and Dozy, and they were all known to have been in Criss Cross Station that morning. For various reasons into which it is not necessary to go, it can be taken as certain that one of them was guilty.

Two lines meet at Criss Cross. One of them goes from W through Criss Cross to X, and the other one goes from Y through Criss Cross to Z. The trains only run once an hour on these lines and the relevant details are as follows:

W	10:11	X	10:11
Criss Cross (Arr)	10:29	Criss Cross (Arr)	10:26
(Dep)	10:33	(Dep)	10:29
X	10:46	W	10:49

Y	10:09	Z	10:03
Criss Cross (Arr)	10:23	Criss Cross (Arr)	10:22
(Dep)	10:25	(Dep)	10:25
Z	10:53	Y	10:43

The distances of W, X, Y, and Z by road from Criss Cross are 4 mi, 5 mi, 5 mi, and 7 mi, respectively. The areas between W, X, Y, and Z are covered by sea, impenetrable swamps, impassable mountains, and notices saying "Private, no entrance." It is therefore not possible for anyone to get from one of these places to another without passing through Criss Cross either by road or by train.

The 4 suspects make statements, all true, as follows:

Quick: I was in Y at 10:12 and in X at 10:47.
Racy: I was in X at 10:10 and in Z at 10:55.
Sleepy: I was in W at 10:13 and in Y at 10:52.
Dozy: I was in Z at 10:02 and in W at 10:45.

I'm afraid they tend rather to use each other's bicycles or any that they can find, and it may be taken as certain that if a bicycle is wanted, one is available. When cycling they move at a steady speed of 15 mi/h.

The doctor was seen alive at 10:28, and his corpse was discovered at 10:33. The Professor reckoned, and I am sure he was right, that the murderer would have needed at least 2 min to do the deed.

What were the exact movements of all 4 suspects?

Who killed Doctor Dope?

35. The Multiplication That Was Worse Than Vexation (*****)

"We have dealt," said Professor Knowall to me one morning, "with many different kinds of puzzles, but I don't think we have ever yet had a multiplication sum with letters substituted for digits. That would seem to me," he went on, "a case—if I may coin a phrase—of multiplication becoming vexation."

I was not in a very good mood that morning. My housekeeper had left me and I had had to make my own bed. At the thought of a multiplication sum with letters substituted for digits something seemed to snap inside me.

"Don't you ever have enough?" I found myself asking. "We have had addition, subtraction, and division with silly letters substituted for crazy digits, all in the hope of making us better detectives. Will you please explain to me how multiplication with letters for digits is going to assist me to catch more criminals? If you ask me," I said, "which I know you don't—you never do—it is all in aid of Professor Knowall showing everyone what a clever chap he is. Or to put it even more plainly, . . ." And then I stopped. There are some things that one cannot say however much one loses one's cool.

There was what seemed to me to be a pregnant silence that I thought would never end.

"We might, of course, call it the multiplication that is worse than vexation," the Professor went on, with his eyes and no doubt his mind on his puzzle.

I think my outburst had done me good, for I now felt calm and relaxed, but I must admit that I was rather glad that, as usual, the Professor clearly had not heard what I said. To lose my housekeeper and my job on the same day would have been disaster indeed.

"Perhaps you might like to try it, my dear Sergeant Simple," he said, "it's not as hard as you might think."

In my relaxed frame of mind I was prepared to try anything, and I think that my acting ability was sufficient to persuade the Professor that I really was doing my best.

The multiplication sum the Professor put in front of me had

the digits replaced by letters, with the same letter standing for the same digit wherever it appeared and different letters standing for different digits. It looked like this:

$$\begin{array}{c} \text{T M B T P M G} \\ \underline{\text{T}} \\ \hline \text{G E D E E X T G} \end{array}$$

"All you have to do now," said the Professor, "is to write the sum out with the silly letters replaced by the crazy digits. You ought not to find that too difficult, my very dear Sergeant."

My mind was in a turmoil. What exactly had I said? It was a turmoil that it took me a long time to get rid of, but I felt I had to do it. It was a matter of contrast, I suppose, but once I had gotten rid of that, the puzzle didn't really seem to be too hard. And I did it! Can you?

36. "Four Tribes Are Better Than Three" (**)

Once more Professor Knowall and I visited the Island of Imperfection. This time, I am glad to say, it really was a holiday. The sun shone, the inhabitants of the Island were as charming and as unpredictable as ever—in fact, even more so, for the first thing we discovered was that there is now another tribe on the Island, which gave the Professor great satisfaction.

"Four tribes, my dear Sergeant Simple," he said, "are undoubtedly better than 3, the fourth one has a different truth-telling rule, and we shall have to exercise our brains more than ever. What better way could there be of spending a holiday?"

In fact I could think of many better ways of spending a holiday, bathing in the sea, for example, with some rather nice Shilli-Shalla girls who greeted us with great pleasure when we arrived. But—and I have to keep saying this—the Professor is my boss and I have to pay a great deal of attention to his idiosyncrasy.

It wasn't long before the Professor was faced with the puzzle for which he had been longing. But I had better explain the background.

There used to be 3 tribes on the Island: the Pukkas, who always told the truth; the Wotta-Woppas, who never told the truth; and the Shilli-Shallas, who made statements alternately true and false or false and true. The fourth tribe is called the Jokers, and all that we could discover about their truth-telling rules was that in making 3 statements, these were any rules that were different from those of any of the other 3 tribes.

This story deals with 4 men, one from each tribe. In the interview that was obviously essential for us to discover the tribes to which they belonged only 3 of them were present. There they were in front of us, sun-tanned and charming. They spoke as follows:

A: 1. C sometimes makes a true statement.
B: 1. D is a Shilli-Shalla.
C: 1. D is a Pukka.
   2. B is a Pukka.
   3. I am a Joker.

And D was not to be found. In fact, I think D was almost certainly in that wonderful sea, where I longed to be myself.

I felt rather inclined to make some jokes about the Joker, but I had a feeling that the Professor would not be amused, so I contented myself with making a few encouraging remarks and doing my best to ensure that the Professor only saw an eager face.

Perhaps it would not be quite fair to say that my method worked, but it did not take long for the Professor to decide to which tribe A, B, C, and D belonged. Can you?

PART V

Letters for Digits:
Addition and
Multiplication
(37–40)

37. Addition: Letters for Digits (Two Numbers) (**)

In the addition sum below, letters have been substituted for digits. The same letter stands for the same digit wherever it appears and different letters stand for different digits.

```
K R A M Y R
K Q E M Y R
―――――――――――
Y A H E K Y
═══════════
```

Write the sum out with numbers substituted for letters.

38. Addition: Letters for Digits (Four Numbers) (****)

In the addition sum below, letters have been substituted for digits. The same letter stands for the same digit wherever it appears and different letters stand for different digits.

```
K B R A K P
P H R E P K
K M R D X P
K B R E K X
―――――――――――
H P H D E E
═══════════
```

Write the sum out with numbers substituted for letters.

61

39. Addition: Letters for Digits (Four of Them Missing) (***)

It is, I admit, a pretty moot point whether it is better to guess at some of Uncle Bungle's illegible letters and hope for the best or just to leave them out. For some time now I have guessed, but I must admit that my guessing is not what it was, so in this sum anything that is illegible has just been left out. Letters stand for digits, the same letter stands for the same digit whenever it appears, and different letters stand for different digits. In the final sum all the digits from 0 to 9 are included.

```
  G T K T G P K M
  — K — D — P — M
  _____
  M G M P K P M M T
  ═══════════════
```

Write out the correct addition sum.

40. Multiplication: Letters for Digits (***)

In the multiplication sum below the digits have been replaced by letters. The same letter stands for the same digit whenever it appears and different letters stand for different digits.

```
  Y M G Y B M P
              P
  _____
  P A X H E B Y
  ═════════════
```

Write the sum out with letters replaced by digits.

PART VI

Soccer

(41–46)

41. Old Method (Four Teams) (*)

Four soccer teams—A, B, C, and D—are to play each other once. After some, or perhaps all of the matches have been played, a table giving some details of matches played, won, lost, etc., looked like this:

Team	Played	Won	Lost	Drawn	Goals for	Goals against	Points
A						4	3
B						2	
C					2	3	0
D							5

(Two points are given for a win, and 1 for a draw.)
Find the score in each match.

42. Bangle Blunders Yet Again (**)

Uncle Bungle has just made up another soccer puzzle, in which 3 teams were to play each other once. After some, or perhaps all of the matches had been played, my uncle produced a table giving some details of matches played, won, lost, etc. It looked like this:

Team	Played	Won	Lost	Drawn	Goals for	Goals against	Points
A					2	2	1
B					5	3	
C	2					3	0

(Two points are given for a win, and 1 to each side for a draw.)
One of the troubles about Uncle Bungle, however—and no doubt there are many things about him that are not as they should be—is that he is nearly always in a hurry and he just will not *check*. He was so pleased with this puzzle that he copied it out carelessly, or perhaps he could not read his own writing, and *1* of the figures is wrong.

Which figure is wrong?
What was the score in each match?

43. More Goals and More Attractive Soccer (***)

The new and better method of rewarding goals in soccer goes from strength to strength. In this method, 10 points are awarded for a win, 5 points for a draw, and 1 point for every goal scored.

In a recent competition between 3 teams A, B and C, who each played each other once, A got 20 points, B got 5, and C got 19. Some idea of the success of this method (although it is still of course in its early stages) can be deduced from the fact that each side scored at least 1 goal in every match.

Find the score in each match.

44. Uncle Bungle's New Soccer Puzzle (Letters for Digits) (**)

As if the soccer puzzles which Uncle Bungle has been making up for many years were not enough for him and for everybody else, he has been producing a new type, in which figures are replaced by letters. How crazy can people get!

In this particular puzzle 4 teams are going to play each other once. The figures written in the table below give the situation when some of the matches have been played. The digits from 0 to 9 are replaced by letters, and each letter stands for the same digit wherever it appears, and different letters stand for different digits. I am happy to record that on this occasion Uncle has not made a mistake and all is as it should be.

The table looked like this:

Team	Played	Won	Lost	Drawn	Goals for	Goals against	Points
A	x			k	h	p	
B		h			m	m	
C	p	x	h	k	t		m
D	k						

(Two points are given for a win and 1 point to each side in a drawn match.)

Find the score in each match.

66

45. Letters for Digits (Five Teams) (***)

Five soccer teams (A, B, C, D, and E) are to play each other once. After some of the matches had been played, a table giving some details of the numbers won, lost, drawn, etc., was drawn up.

Unfortunately all was not as it should be. Not only were there a lot of gaps in the table, but also the digits had been replaced by letters. I was able to discover that each letter stood for the same digit (from 0 to 9) whenever it appears and that different letters stood for different digits.

The table looked like this:

Team	Played	Won	Lost	Drawn	Goals for	Goals against	Points
A	x		h	h	p	r	
B		m		p	t		g
C	h				x	m	
D	r				y	k	r
E				p	m	g	

(Two points are given for a win and 1 point to each side in a drawn match.)

Find the score in each match.

46. Soccer and Addition: Letters for Digits (****)

In the following soccer table and addition sum, letters have been substituted for digits (from 0 to 9). The same letter stands for the same digit whenever it appears, and different letters stand for different digits. The 4 teams eventually play each other once.

(i)

Team	Played	Won	Lost	Drawn	Goals for	Goals against	Points
A				x	m	k	x
B	j				m	t	
C	x				j	m	
D	m				h		t

(ii)
$$
\begin{array}{r}
k\ x \\
p\ j \\
\hline
h\ m \\
\hline
\end{array}
$$

(Two points are given for a win, and 1 point to each side in a drawn match.)

Find the score in the soccer matches and write the addition sum out with numbers substituted for letters.

PART VII

Cross-Number Puzzles

(47–48)

47. A Cross Number (3 by 3) (**)

(There are no 0's.)

Across

1. An odd number. The sum of the digits is half the sum of the digits of 5 across.
4. The sum of the digits is 8.
5. Reversed, a multiple of 6.

Down

2. 3 times 4 across.
3. Each digit is greater than the one before by the same amount.

48. A Cross Number (5 by 5) (***)

1	2	3	4	■
5		6		7
8		■	9	
10		11		
■	12			■

(There are no 0's.)

Across

1. Three of these digits are those of 6 across, not necessarily in the same order, and the other one is the sum of the digits of 6 across.
5. A multiple of the square root of 7 down.
6. A perfect cube.
8. A multiple of 23.
9. A prime number when reversed.
10. Each digit is greater than the one before.
12. The sum of the digits is 12.

Down

1. The sum of the digits is the same as the sum of the digits of 3 down.
2. The same when reversed.
3. See 1 down.
4. Each digit is greater than the one before.
7. A perfect square.
8. A multiple of 19.
11. A prime number.

PART VIII

The Island of Imperfection

(49–51)

49. Ages and Shacks on the Island (****)

There are 3 tribes on the Island of Imperfection: the Pukkas, who always tell the truth; the Wotta-Woppas, who never tell the truth; and the Shilli-Shallas, who make statements alternately true and false or false and true.

This story deals with 4 inhabitants of the Island, their ages, and the houses in which they live. As a matter of fact, for "houses" I should really say "shacks," for they have no central heating or modern conveniences and although they have numbers attached to them, they are in fact scattered all over the place. Nevertheless, numbers they do have, and it is those that interest us. We also want to know the ages of the four inhabitants, and there are no complications about them.

It really was a curious coincidence, but it so happened that the more truthful an inhabitant was, the higher was the number of his shack, and that means that it is possible for 2 who are equally truthful to live in the same house. It is also rather curious that the more truthful a person is the younger he is. It follows that the ages and the house numbers of 2 of them could be the same.

Of the 4 people with whom this story deals there is at least 1 from each tribe.

They speak as follows:

A: 1. The number of B's shack is greater than that of mine.
    2. D belongs to a more truthful tribe than I do.
    3. The oldest of us is 49 years older than the youngest of us.

B: 1. A's age is 15 less than the number of D's shack.
    2. Add the ages of the youngest of us and the oldest of us, and you get the number of someone's shack.
    3. D's age is 24 more than the number of someone's shack.

C: 1. A2 is true.
    2. No one lives in Number 1.
    3. B is a Shilli-Shalla.

D: 1. The age of the youngest of us is 17 more than the number of C's shack.
    2. The shack numbers add up to 163.

3. The number of A's shack is greater than that of C's.

Find the tribes to which A, B, C, and D belong, their ages, and the numbers of their shacks.

50. Some Island Soccer (***)

Alf, Bert, and Charlie are still on the Island of Imperfection, and they have become much involved in tribal affairs. One of them is a member of the Pukkas, who always tell the truth; another is a member of the Wotta-Woppas, who never tell the truth; and the third is a member of the Shilli-Shallas, who make statements alternately true and false or false and true. Each tribe has a soccer team, and they have all played each other once.

Alf, Bert, and Charlie (whose teams are referred to as A, B, and C, respectively) make statements, in accordance with their tribal characteristics, as follows:

ALF: 1. The Pukkas beat the Wotta-Woppas.
2. Bert is not a Wotta-Woppa.
3. C scored no goals against B.

BERT: 1. The score in A vs. B was 3–1.
2. Five goals altogether were scored in A's matches.
3. The score in Pukkas vs. Shilli-Shallas was 2–0.

CHARLIE: 1. We were beaten by B.
2. B scored 3 goals altogether.
3. We scored the same number of goals against A as against B.

(If a statement in which a score is given is false, the number of goals scored by *each* side will be incorrect, though the *result* may be correct.)

Find to which tribes Alf, Bert, and Charlie belong and the score in each match.

51. Hopes and Successes (****)

I had been away from the Island of Imperfection for some time and I was amazed—and rather distressed—on a recent visit to find that there was now another tribe there.

But I had better explain. In the old carefree days, which I knew so well, there had been three tribes on the Island: the Pukkas, who always told the truth, the Wotta-Woppas, who never told the truth, and the Shilli-Shallas, who made statements alternatively true and false or false and true. I cannot pretend to know how it happened, but now there is another tribe who call themselves the Jokers. I am afraid that all I can tell you about them is that in making 3 statements their truth-telling rules are any rules that are different from those of the other 3 tribes. Just to be different! That seems to be all they are interested in, and I find it hard to restrain myself from making some acid comments about the modern generation. They don't seem to be much interested in fun or laughter but in achievement. It is no doubt because of this that the main currency of the island is called a Success, and it is made up of 100 Hopes.

The 4 men with whom this story deals, whom I shall call A, B, C, and D (1 from each tribe), make statements as follows:

A: 1. B makes more true statements than D does.
    2. My income is 7 Successes and 50 Hopes more or less than D's income.
    3. C is a Wotta-Woppa.
B: 1. A's income is 2 Successes and 50 Hopes more or less than mine.
    2. D2 is true.
    3. C's income is 8 Successes and 50 Hopes.
C: 1. D is a Joker.
    2. My income is 10 Successes.
    3. B is a Pukka.
D: 1. B is a Joker.
    2. My income is 1 Success more or less than C's income.
    3. C is not a Joker.

It was rather interesting to notice that the more truthful a man was, the less was his income. All their incomes were multiples of 50 Hopes.

Find the tribes to which A, B, C, and D belong and their weekly incomes.

Solutions

1. We Compete. Who Does What?

Fill in the possibilities of statements 1, 2, 3, and 4, and we get:

1				Worker		DO	DS	BW
2	B		A	Worker		DO		BW
3	B		E	Worker	DKP		DS	BW
4	B	C	A	E	DKP			
5		C	E		DKP		DS	

From statement 1, Worker cannot be lower than third, B cannot be higher than second or lower than fourth, and DKP cannot be higher than third.

Neither A, B, C, nor E can be first. Since D is not mentioned, D is first. And the DKP is fourth (no one else can be). ∴ from 1, Worker is second and B is third. Since Worker is 2nd, the DO is first (the only possibility). ∴ C is fourth (see 2). ∴ the BW is third and E is fifth (see 4). A cannot be fourth; ∴ A is second. The DS must then be fifth.

Complete Solution

1. Duggie (Door-Opener)
2. Alf (Worker)
3. Bert (Bottle-Washer)
4. Charlie (Door-Knob-Polisher)
5. Ernie (Door-Shutter)

2. How Tall and How Heavy?

Denote Height by H and Weight by W. Then the following can be said about their possible positions:

	H				W			
1	A							E
2		B	C		A	B	C	E
3	A		C	E			C	E
4		B	C	E	A	B	C	E
5	A			E			C	

Note that D's places add up to 7; ∴ D cannot be first in H or W (1 + 6 is not possible). ∴ A is first in H and E is first in W.

C cannot be fifth in W, for the difference between E and C in W is the same as the difference between C and E in H, and C is not first in H. ∴ D is fifth in W (no one else can be); ∴ D is second in H. ∴ B is fourth in H (the only place left for B); ∴ B is fourth in W and A is second in W. E is fifth in H (no one else can be). And C is third in H and W.

Complete Solution

  Height: 1. Alf, 2. Duggie, 3. Charlie, 4. Bert, 5. Ernie
  Weight: 1. Ernie, 2. Alf, 3. Charlie, 4. Bert, 5. Duggie

3. Men-only Mews

Let B's number be x, then D's number is $3x$. Since B's number is 9 less than A's, A's is $x + 9$. Since A's number is odd, x is even. A's is 23 more than E's; $\therefore$ E's is $(x + 9 - 23)$, i.e., $x - 14$. And C's is $\frac{1}{2}(3x + x) = 2x$.

If E's number is 1, then $x - 14$ would be 1 and x would be 15. But x is even; $\therefore$ E's number must be even.

Suppose E's number is 2. Then $x = 16$, $\therefore$ B's number is 16. $\therefore$ $3x = 48$, $\therefore$ D's number is 48. $2x = 32$, $\therefore$ C's number is 32. $x + 9 = 25$, $\therefore$ A's number is 25.

If E's number is 4 (remember it must be even), then x would be 18, and $3x$ would be 54—which is not possible. $\therefore$ E's number must be 2.

Complete Solution

A = 25
B = 16
C = 32
D = 48
E = 2

4. The Puzzle of Life

Let A's and B's ages *now* be A and B. Then

$$A = 2(B + 10) \qquad \text{(i)}$$

Let ". . . when B is "Three times . . ." be denoted by C. Then

$$C = 3(A - 21) \qquad \text{(ii)}$$

$$\therefore C = 3[2(B + 10) - 21] = 3(2B + 20 - 21) = 3(2B - 1) \text{ (iii)}$$

∴ C is 3 times an odd number. ∴ is odd and is a multiple of 3.

"When B is three times . . . , then the two digits of his age will add to nine. . . ." Therefore, C is a two-figure number such that the sum of the digits is 9. (And it is odd and a multiple of 3.) ∴ C could be 81, 63, 45, 27.

If C = 27, then from (i), 27 = 3(A − 21); ∴ A = 30. ∴ 21 years ago A would have been 9—not possible, for A was not less than 10.

If C = 63, then from (ii), 63 = 3(A − 21); ∴ A = 42. ∴ 21 years ago A would have been 21—not possible for A "was still a minor." ∴ C is not 63.

If C = 81, A would have been more than 21. ∴ C can only be 45.

∴ from (iii), B = 8 and from (i) A = 36.

Complete Solution

A = 36
B = 8

5. "Uncle Bungle's Writing Is Not a Pretty Sight"

X	A	X	F	K	K	K	K	
K	T	D	H	F	K	K	K	
–	A	–	X	–	K	–	K	(ix)
P	T	T	F	D	K	K	K	
A	R	M	R	–	P	P	P	

(i) (ii) (iii) (iv) (v) (vi) (vii) (viii)

In (i), X + K + – + P + (perhaps) something that has been carried from (ii) must be 9 or less. [Notice that it would not make sense for the first blank in (ix) to be 0, though some of the other blanks may be.]

From (viii), P must be even (K + K + K + K). ∴ since it also appears in (i), it must be 2 or 4 [not 6 or 8, for 1 + 2 + 1 + 6 = 10].

If P in (viii) were 2, then K would have been 3 (3 + 3 + 3 + 3 = 12). There would be 1 to carry to (vii). ∴ (vii) could only be 3 + 3 + 2 + 3 + 1 (carried) = 12. There would then be 1 to carry to (vi). But this is not possible since 3 + 3 + 3 + 3 + 1 (carried) = 13. It is clear that a similar argument applies whenever there is anything to carry from (viii). ∴ P cannot be 2, it must be 4. ∴ K must be 1. The blank in (vii) then must be 1.

In (i), K = 1 and P = 4; ∴ X must be at least 2 and the blank must be 1 or 2. ∴ A is at least 8. Since we have A + A in (ii), there must be at least 1 to carry. ∴ A must be 9, and there is only 1 to carry. ∴ X in (i) is 2, and the blank is 1. ∴ T in (ii) must be 0, R must be 8 (9 + 0 + 9 + 0 = 18), and there cannot be anything to carry from (iii).

In (iii), M cannot be more than 7, and D must be at least 3. If D were 5, then (iv) would be at least 3 + 6 + 2 + 3, so that there would be 1 to carry to (iii). ∴ D cannot be 5, for 2 + 5 + 0 + 0 + 1 (carried) = 8, and we have seen that M cannot be more than 7. ∴ D must be 3, and M must be 6 or 7.

In (iv) we have F + H + 2 + F + ? [carried from (v)] = 18. (It is easy to see that it could not be 28.) ∴ 2F + H + ? (carried) = 16.

85

(The digits left are 5 and 6 or 7.) Suppose that F = 6. Then H would be at least 5. But 6 + 6 + 5 = 17, which is too much. ∴ F must be 5, and H must be 6 (not 7, for 5 + 5 + 7 = 17). ∴ M in (iii) can only be 7, and the blank in (iii) must be 1.

Consider (v). We have 1 + 5 + − + 3 = − [and we know that there is nothing to carry from (vi) to (v) or from (v) to (iv)]. ∴ it can only be 1 + 5 + 0 + 3 = 9.

Complete Solution

```
2 9 2 5 1 1 1 1
1 0 3 6 5 1 1 1
1 9 1 2 0 1 1 1
4 0 0 5 3 1 1 1
───────────────
9 8 7 8 9 4 4 4
═══════════════
```

6. Crazy Crescent

Their statements can be simplified thus:

 (i) (A) $A - B = 12$
 (ii) (B) $D + A = 2C$
 (iii) (C) $C = 3E$
 (iv) (D) $B - D = 13$
 (v) (E) $A = 47$

We know that *one* of these is wrong.
Consider (i), (ii), and (iv).

From (i)	$A - B = 12$
and from (iv)	$B - D = 13$
Add:	$A - D = 25$
From (ii)	$A + D = 2C$
Add:	$2A = 25 + 2C$

This is not possible since $25 + C$ must be odd and $2A$ is even. $\therefore$ one of (i), (ii), and (iv) must be wrong. $\therefore$ (iii) and (v) must be correct.

 Suppose (i) is wrong. ($A - B = 12$). Then $A = 47$. Suppose that $D = 1$. Then from (iv), $B = 14$; from (ii), $C = 24$; and from (iii), $E = 8$. Thus $E = 8$, $C = 24$, $A = 47$, $D = 1$, $B = 14$. E can go up by 1. Thus: $E = 9$, $C = 27$, $A = 47$, $D = 7$, $B = 20$. C goes up and is always a multiple of 3 ($3m$); D is 1 more than $6m$; B is 2 more than $6m$; A is 47 (5 more than $6m$); and E goes up by 1 from 8. $\therefore$ none of them can be the same until $E = 47$. C would then be 138, but there are only 100 houses in the road. $\therefore$ there is no solution if (i) is wrong.

 Suppose (iv) is wrong ($B - D = 13$), and the rest are correct. Then $A = 47$; and from (i), $B = 35$. Suppose that $D = 1$; then from (ii), $C = 24$; and from (iii), $E = 8$. Thus: $E = 8$, $C = 24$, $A = 47$, $D = 1$, $B = 35$. E can go up by 1. Thus: $E = 9$, $C = 27$, $A = 47$, $D = 7$, $B = 35$. C goes up and is always $3m$, D is 1 more than $m(6)$, A is 47 (5 more than $6m$), and B is 35 (5 more than $6m$).

E goes up by 1 from 8. ∴ none of them can be the same until E = 35. C would then be 105. But there are only 100 houses in the road. ∴ there is no solution if (iv) is wrong. Suppose (ii) is wrong. (D + A = 2C), and the rest are correct. Then A = 47; from (i), B = 35; from (iv), D = 22. We know that C = 3E, but we have no other information about C or E. A, B, and D are not 3m, ∴ they cannot be the same as C. But E can be any number starting from 1; ∴ E can be 22 (and D is 22), and C would then be 66. (If E were equal to B(35), C would be more than 100.)

Complete Solution

Alf	47
Bert	35
Charlie	66
Duggie	22
Ernie	22

7. Some Missing Figures

```
              2 -                    (i)
      - - ) - - - -                  (ii)
            - -                      (iii)
            ___
            - - -                    (iv)
          3 - -                      (v)
          =====
```

The divisor must start with 3 or more, for otherwise it would not have been necessary to have 3 figures in (iv) and (v). ∴ (iii), which is twice the divisor, must start at least with 6. It cannot start with more than 6, for 6 + 3 = 9, and the first figure of (ii) cannot be more than 9. ∴ the divisor is 3 –. It must be more than 33, for 33 × 9 is only 297 and (v) starts with 3. It must be less than 35, for 35 × 2 = 70, and we know that (iii) must start with 6. ∴ the divisor is 34. And (v) must be 34 × 9, i.e., 306.

Add up from the bottom and we get:

Complete Solution

```
              2 9
      3 4 ) 9 8 6
            6 8
            ___

            3 0 6
            3 0 6
            =====
```

8. Four, Five, Six, Seven

```
                - - -                        (i)
    4 - ) 6 - - -                            (ii)
          - 7                                (iii)
          ___
                - - -                        (iv)
          5 - -                              (v)
          ===
```

We must first find the figure that is wrong. The first figure in (iii) must be 5 or 6 [for there is no figure below it in (iv)]. ∴ 4 and 6 cannot both be right. 49 × 9 = 441. ∴ the 4 in the divisor and the 5 in (v) cannot both be right. ∴ the 4 in the divisor is wrong. (It is the number common to 4 and 6 and to 4 and 5.) ∴ the other 3 figures are correct. ∴ the first figure in (iv) is 5; ∴ the second figure in (ii) is 2. ∴ (iii) is 57 [not 19—see (iv) and (v)]. ∴ (iv) and (v) are 513 (57 × 9).

Add up from the bottom and we get:

Complete Solution

```
                1 0 9
    5 7 ) 6 2 1 3
          5 7
          ___
          5 1 3
          5 1 3
          ===
```

9. A Common Incorrectness

```
                    1 6 - 2      (i)
          2 9 ) - 0 0 - - 8      (ii)
                  8 6            (iii)
                  ―――――
                  2 - -          (iv)
                  1 2 5          (v)
                  ―――――
                    3 - -        (vi)
                    2 4 8        (vii)
                    ―――――
                        9 6      (viii)
                        3 5      (ix)
                        ════
```

(The reader is advised to have a figure like that below in which to fill the correct figures as they are discovered.)

```
                    - - - -      (i)
        - - ) - - - - - - -      (ii)
              - -              (iii)
              ―――――
              - - -              (iv)
              - - -              (v)
              ―――――
                - - -            (vi)
                - - -            (vii)
                ―――――
                    - -          (viii)
                    - -          (ix)
                    ════
```

(iii) cannot be divisor (see *1* in (i)), ∴ *divisor is less than 50.* If divisor starts with 1 then (v) would start with *1* (19 × 9 = 171). But 1 is figure given. ∴ divisor does not start with 1, nor does it start with *2* (figure given). ∴ divisor *starts with 3 or 4.* Divisor goes into (iii) 2 or 3 times. *Suppose 3,* then divisor must be 30, 31, 32 or 33. Then (viii) and (ix) must be divisor times 1 or 3 (not *2* for this is figure given in (i)). ∴ (viii) and (ix) must start with 3 or 9. But it

91

does not for these are figures given. ∴ *divisor goes into (iii) twice only.*

Suppose divisor starts with 3. 1st figure in (ii) must be 1, and next figures are *not* 00. ∴ (ii) starts 111 (at least). *And divisor must be more than 37, otherwise it would go 3 times into 111.*

If divisor were 38, 2nd figure in (iii) would be 6, *but it is not,* ∴ divisor *not* 38. And divisor is not 39 for 9 is figure given, ∴ divisor is *4*−. ∴ (iii) starts with 8 or 9, but not 8 for this is figure given, ∴ *9.* ∴ divisor is *45*+.

Divisor goes into (ix) *once* (not twice, for 2 is figure given). ∴ 2nd figure of divisor cannot be *5* (figure given in (ix)), nor *6* (figure given in (viii)), nor *8* (for 8 is last figure in (ii), nor 9 (for this is 2nd figure of divisor). ∴ *divisor is 47,* and (iii) is *94,* and (viii) and (ix) are *47.*

It will be convenient to put down the multiples of *47,* thus:

$$
\begin{aligned}
47 \times 1 &= 47 \\
\times 2 &= 94 \\
\times 3 &= 141 \\
\times 4 &= 188 \\
\times 5 &= 235 \\
\times 6 &= 282 \\
\times 7 &= 329 \\
\times 8 &= 376 \\
\times 9 &= 423
\end{aligned}
$$

(vi) and (vii) differ by less than 10; ∴ as we can see from figure above they must start with same figure. ∴ (vii) must be either 141 or 188 or 423 (they cannot start with 2 or 3 (figure given)). But not 141 and not 188 (4 and 8 figures given). ∴ *423.*

(v) does not start with 1, ∴ it must be 47×5 (235), or 47×6 (282) or 47×7 (329), or 47×8 (376), or 47×9 (423). But not 47×5 (5 is given as 3rd figure); and not 47×6 (6 in (i)); and not 47×7 (2 is given as 2nd figure); and not 47×9 (2 is 2nd figure) ∴ *47 × 8 (376)*

Add up from the bottom and we can fill in all the figures:

Complete Solution

```
                2 8 9 1
        47 ) 1 3 5 8 7 7
             9 4
             ─────
               4 1 8
               3 7 6
               ─────
                 4 2 7
                 4 2 3
                 ─────
                     4 7
                     4 7
                     ═══
```

10. Letters for Digits

$$
\begin{array}{r}
s\ b\ p\ x \\
s\ p\ )\ \overline{b\ r\ d\ x\ r\ d} \\
x\ q\ s
\end{array}
$$

	s b p x	(i)
s p)	b r d x r d	(ii)
	x q s	(iii)
	x t x	(iv)
	t p t	(v)
	c t r	(vi)
	b y y	(vii)
	t t d	(viii)
	t t c	(ix)
	x	(x)

(It will help to have a diagram with blanks replacing the letters, so that the figures can be filled in as they are found.) From the first figures of (iv) and (v), $x - t = 1$, and from the last figures of (iv) and (v), $x - t = t$. $\therefore t = 1$ and $x = 2$. From (ii) and (iii), $b = 3$, $\therefore$ from (vi) and (vii), $c = 4$.

From (ix), we know that $11- = 2 \times (s\ p)$. $\therefore s = 5$. From (viii), (ix), and (x), $d = 6$. From (iv), (v), and (vi), $p = 7$. $\therefore$ (iii) $= 57 \times 5 = 285$; $\therefore q = 8$. $\therefore$ from (ii), (iii), and (iv), $r = 0$. (vii) $= 57 \times 7 = 399$. $\therefore y = 9$.

Complete Solution

$$
\begin{array}{r}
5\ 3\ 7\ 2 \\
5\ 7\ )\ \overline{3\ 0\ 6\ 2\ 0\ 6} \\
2\ 8\ 5 \\
\hline
2\ 1\ 2 \\
1\ 7\ 1 \\
\hline
4\ 1\ 0 \\
3\ 9\ 9 \\
\hline
1\ 1\ 6 \\
1\ 1\ 4 \\
\hline
2
\end{array}
$$

11. Some Letters for Digits, Some Digits Missing

```
              k -                    (i)
      k - ) k - - -                  (ii)
            - - -                    (iii)
           _____
              - -                    (iv)
              - -                    (v)
           =======
```

Suppose k were 5. Then the divisor could not be more than 59 and (iii) would then be 59×5, i.e., 295. It would not then be possible for the first digit of (ii) to be 5. $\therefore k$ cannot be 5, and it is easy to see that it cannot be less than 5.

Suppose k were 8. Then the divisor could not be more than 89 and (iii) would then be 89×8, i.e., 712. But if the first digit of (ii) is to be 8, there would have to be another digit in (iv) before the 2 digits given. Clearly k cannot be 6 or 7. $\therefore k$ must be 9.

Suppose the divisor were 98. Then (iii) would be 98×9, i.e., 882. Again there would have to be another digit in (iv) before the 2 digits given. $\therefore$ the divisor cannot be 98, but must be more. $\therefore$ the divisor can only be 99. $\therefore$ (iii) is 99×9, i.e., 891. Since the divisor is 99, (iv) and (v) must both be 99.

Complete Solution

```
               9 1
      9 9 ) 9 0 0 9
            8 9 1
           _____
              9 9
              9 9
           =======
```

12. Car Trouble

Denote:

    Left door by A
    Right door by B
    Left window by C
    Right window by D
    Sliding roof by E
    Ash tray by F
    Rattle by R

Then

   (i) $A, D, E, F \rightarrow R$
  (ii) $A, B, E \rightarrow R$
 (iii) $B, E, F \rightarrow R$

Note that in (i) and (ii) we listed those items that are not mentioned, which lead to R continuing, and in (iii) we put down those items that are mentioned and whose "fixing" led to R stopping.

Complete Solution

Sliding roof [E is the only one which appears in (i), (ii), and (iii)].

13. Why D Was Dumb

Suppose that C1 is true. Then A would be a W-W. ∴ A2 would be false. In that case C would never tell the truth. ∴ C1 would not be true. ∴ Our assumption is incorrect and C1 is false. ∴ A was not a W-W.

Suppose that B2 is true. Then since A is not a W-W, A would be a Sh-Sh, and C would be a Pukka, but that is not possible since C1 is false. ∴ B2 must be false. ∴ A must be a Pukka (no one else can be). ∴ B did it. Since A2 is true, C must be a Sh-Sh, and B must be a W-W. ∴ C2 is true, and D was over 40.

Complete Solution

B did it.
D was over 40.
A is a Pukka.
B is a Wotta-Woppa.
C is a Shilli-Shalla.

14. Titus in a Tizzy

Let us consider the different ways of expressing the logic of

(i) "If p, then q."

It is equivalent to

(ii) "If not q, then not p."

(If it were p, it would have to be q.) These are also equivalent to

(iii) "It cannot be both p and not q."

(As we have seen, if it were p, it would be q.) The fourth way of expressing this may be seen most easily by considering the statement:

"Either Smith, or Jones, or both must be present."

If Smith is not present, Jones must be; and if Jones is not present, Smith must be. In other words:

"If not p (Smith), then q (Jones)."

If we now write "p" for "not p" and "not p" for "p," we see that "If p, then q" is equivalent to

(iv) "Either not p or q, or both."

B = Finding bicycle
C(1) = Coal shed
C(2) = Cycle shed
D = Dining room table
F = Front porch

We have

1. Either not C(1) or not B; or If C(1), then not B.
2. If B, then not D; or If D, then not B.
3. If not B, then not F; or If F, then B.
4. Not both B and C(2); or If C(2), then not B.

Clearly, 3 is what we want; B is in F.

Complete Solution

Titus should look in the front porch.

15. Getting the Professor to the Point

$$
\begin{array}{ccc}
3 & 0 & 7 \quad \text{(iv)} \\
2 & 3 & 7 \quad \;\;\text{(v)} \\
\hline
7 & 3 & 2 \quad \text{(vi)} \\
\hline
\end{array}
$$

(i) (ii) (iii)

Consider (ii): Since the two 3's are the same, 0 must stand for 9 and there must be 1 to carry from (iii) to (ii) and from (ii) to (i). (The only other possibility would be for 0 to stand for 0, but this is not allowed.) As far as we know at the moment the 3 can stand for anything except 3 or 9. In (iii), 2 must stand for an even number [not 0, for it would not make sense to have 0 at the beginning of (v)]. $\therefore$ 2 must stand for 4, 6, or 8. But not 4, for the 7's in (iii) would then stand for 7; and not 8, for the 7's in (iii) would then stand for 9 (9 + 9 = 18) and we know that 0 stands for 9. $\therefore$ 2 stands for 6. $\therefore$ 7 stands for 8 (8 + 8 = 16). There is 1 to carry from (ii) to (i). $\therefore$ 3 in (i) must stand for 1 (1 + 6 + 1 = 8).

Complete Solution

$$
\begin{array}{ccc}
1 & 9 & 8 \\
6 & 1 & 8 \\
\hline
8 & 1 & 6 \\
\hline
\end{array}
$$

16. Let There Be No C

Consider first (v)–(ix). By looking first at (vi), (vii), and (ix), where C is not present, we see that C could not be caused by any one of p, q, r, s, t. ∴ it must be caused by two or more events:

p, r cannot cause C [see (viii)].
p, t cannot cause C [see (vi)].
r, s cannot cause C [see (viii)].
s, t cannot cause C [see (ix)].

∴ r, t cause C. ∴ if we can eliminate either r or t (or both), we shall prevent C from happening. From (iv), r is not caused by J, L, or M; and from (ii), r is not caused by K or N. From (iv), t is not caused by J, L, or M; and from (iii), t is not caused by K. ∴ t is caused by N.

Complete Solution

Elimination of N will eliminate t and thus C.

17. One and One Make Two

Since not more than 7 goals were scored in any match, C must have played 3 (15 goals were scored). ∴ C played all the others.

We know that A lost 0, drew 1, and had 3 goals for and 3 against. ∴ they could not have won any, for goals for would then be greater than goals against. ∴ A only played 1, which must have been against C (who played everyone), with a score of 3–3.

B played 2; ∴ they must have played D as well as C. A, B, and C did not lose a match, but B won 1 and C must have won at least 1 (goals for 9, goals against 6). ∴ D lost both matches. ∴ B versus C was a draw. Since C had 6 goals against and none of them were scored by D, the score in C vs. B was 3–3 and score in C vs. D was 3–0. ∴ score in D vs. B was 0–1.

Complete Solution

A vs. C	3–3
B vs. C	3–3
B vs. D	1–0
C vs. D	3–0

18. The Washing Machine That Didn't

The facts are as follows:

  (i) D, E is followed by q, r.
 (ii) B, C, E is followed by q, s, t.
(iii) A, C, D is followed by p, t.

Notice that if we want to trace the cause of say, q, we direct our attention first to the situations from which q is absent. Thus we know that it cannot be A, C, or D. Since in (i), B cannot be the cause of q, it must be E that appears in (i) and (ii).

Using similar arguments, we get:

A is followed by p.
E is followed by q.
B is followed by s.
C is followed by t.

But none of A, B, C, D, nor E can be the cause of r. Nor can we put the situation right by crossing out D or E in (i). ∴ we must add another cause, F, in (i).

Complete Solution

Another cause, say, F, should be added to (i). Then

p is caused by A.
q is caused by E.
r is caused by F.
s is caused by B.
t is caused by C.

19. The Professor Versus the Knaves

Suppose $x = 1$. Then B, who won x, would have had to have played 2 to make the total of matches even. A had x points, so would have drawn 1 (against B). B cannot have drawn both their matches, for if they had, their goals for and against would be the same. ∴ they would have won their match against C, for their points (t) must be greater than 1.

∴ C would have lost their only match against B. ∴ C's points (p) would be 0. Since B had no goals against, C vs. B would be 0 –? But this is not possible, for p and r would then both stand for the same digit. ∴ x cannot be 1, and since it cannot be 0, x must be 2. ∴ B won 2 matches; ∴ $t = 4$. ∴ 3 matches were played, and since A got 2 points (x) and B got 4 points (t), C's points must be 0. ∴ $p = 0$.

Consider B's matches. Since they won them both, r must be at least 2. But $x = 2$. ∴ r must be 3 or 5 or more ($t = 4$). Suppose r were 5. Then goals for would be $(4 + 5 + 5)$, i.e., 14. Since goals against must be equal to goals for, C's goals against (m) would have to be $(14 - 4 - 0)$, i.e., 10. But m cannot be 10, for each letter stands for a digit (from 0 to 9). ∴ r must be 3, and m must be 6.

Since B had no goals against, B vs. A is ? – 0 and B vs. C is ? – 0. ∴ A vs. B is 0 – ?, and A vs. C is 4 – ? ∴ C vs. A is ? – 4 and C vs. B is 0 – ? And since C had 3 (r) goals for and 6 (m) against, C vs. B is 3 – 4, and C vs. B is 0 – 2. Since B had 3 goals for, B vs. A is 1 – 0.

Complete Solution

A vs. B	0–1
A vs. C	4–3
B vs. C	2–0

20. Just Seven

```
                    - - - - -              (i)
          - - ) - - - - - - - -           (ii)
                - -                        (iii)
                ───
                - - -                      (iv)
                - -                        (v)
                ───
                7 -                        (vi)
                - -                        (vii)
                ───
                - - -                     (viii)
                - - -                      (ix)
                ═══
```

Consider (ii) and (iii). (ii) must start 10, and (iii) must be 9 –.
Consider (iv) and (v). (iv) must be 10 –, and (v) must be 9 –. ∴
since (iv) starts with 1, (ii) must start 100 and (iii) must be 99. ∴
the divisor goes into 99. But it is not 99, since the first figure of
(vii) cannot be 9. And it is not 11. But 11 × 9 = 99, and (viii) and
(ix) have 3 figures. ∴ the divisor is 33. ∴ (iii) and (v) are both 99
and (vii) must be 66. ∴ the first figure in (viii) must be 1, and the
second figure in (vi) must be 6 or more. [Otherwise there would
be no first figure in (viii).] ∴ (viii) starts 10, 12, or 13. But 3 × 33
= 99 and 4 × 33 = 132. ∴ (viii) and (ix) can only be 132.

Add up from the bottom and we get:

Complete Solution

```
                    3 0 3 2 4
        3 3 ) 1 0 0 0 6 9 2
              9 9
              ───
                1 0 6
                  9 9
                  ───
                    7 9
                    6 6
                    ───
                      1 3 2
                      1 3 2
                      ═══
```

21. Saved by the Bell

Note that from "if x, then y" we can deduce "if not y, then not x," but we cannot deduce "if y, then x."

For example, from "if a village is in Sussex, then it is in England" we can deduce that "if a village is *not* in England, then it is *not* in Sussex." But we cannot deduce that "if a village is in England, then it is in Sussex" (for we know that Sussex is only a part of England).

We are told:

  (i) If x is true, then y is false.
 (ii) If z is true, then y is true.
(iii) If z is false, then p is false.

From (iii), if p is true, then z is true. But we are told that p is true, $\therefore$ z is true. $\therefore$ from (ii), since z is true, $\therefore$ y is true.

From (i), "If y is true, then x is false." But we know that y is true. $\therefore$ x is false.

If we are told that p is false, we can come to no conclusion about the truth or falsity of x, y, and z.

Complete Solution

If p is true, then x is false, y is true, and z is true.
If p is false, we can say nothing about x, y, or z.

22. The Sergeant on His Own

```
              a   d   c   d                    (i)
       p d ) m  m   c   f   d   d               (ii)
              e   i                             (iii)
             ─────
              p   e   f                         (iv)
              p   c   m                         (v)
             ─────────
                  m   d   d                     (vi)
                  m   d   c                     (vii)
                 ─────────
                      h   d                      (viii)
                      p   d                      (ix)
                     ─────
                      m   f                      (x)
                     ═════
```

(It will help to have a diagram with blanks replacing the letters so that the figures can be filled in as they are found.)

It is clearly not possible to make much progress until we have discovered more about the incorrect letter.

In (i) d is the second and fourth letter. Both cannot be correct for (v) has 3 letters and (ix) has only 2 letters. ∴ all other letters are correct.

m, the first letter in (ii) can only be 1. Also, since (ix), p d, is the divisor, the fourth letter in (i) should be 1. ∴ it should be m, not d, and this is the mistake.

From (viii), (ix), and (x), $f = 0$. From (iv), (v), and (vi), $d = 9$. From (vii), we know that $9p \times c$ ends in c. ∴ $c = 5$. ∴ the divisor = $195/5 = 39$. ∴ $p = 3$, and in (viii), $h = 4$.

(iii) can only be $39 \times 2 = 78$. ∴ $a = 2$, $e = 7$, and $i = 8$.

Complete Solution

The incorrect letter is the last letter of (i), *d*. It should be *m*.
The correct sum is

```
              2 9 5 1
     3 9 ) 1 1 5 0 9 9
           7 8
           ─────
           3 7 0
           3 5 1
           ─────
             1 9 9
             1 9 5
             ─────
                 4 9
                 3 9
                 ─────
                 1 0
                 ═════
```

23. Blunders from a Blender

We have

   (i) A, C, D are followed by p, r.
  (ii) A, B, D, E are followed by q, r.
 (iii) A, E are followed by q, s.

Further, we are told that the Sergeant has left out 1 small letter.

With the letters as they are, p cannot be caused by A, B, D, or E for in (ii) these letters are not followed by p. But in (i), C is followed by p and in no other case do C and p occur. $\therefore p$ is caused by C.

s occurs only in (iii). It cannot be caused by A or E for there is no s in (ii); $\therefore s$ in (ii) is the letter left out. s is caused by E [not A, for in that case there would be an s in (i)]. We now know that there are no other mistakes.

q occurs in (ii) and (iii); $\therefore$ it must be caused by A or E. But not A, for there is no q in (i). $\therefore q$ is caused by E.

r occurs in (i) and (ii); it must be caused by A or D. But not A, for there is no r in (iii). $\therefore r$ is caused by D.

Complete Solution

The letter left out is in the second bit of evidence. It should be: "A, B, D, E are followed by q, r, s."

  p is caused by C.
  q is caused by E.
  r is caused by D.
  s is caused by E.

24. One Too Many Knots?

"Knots" do not really have much to do with this problem. The fact that the Professor laughed when the Sergeant says that it is a "knotty problem" and goes on to say that he has it "on the best authority" that "there is one too many knots" suggests that we should look at this word again.

Perhaps the Sergeant, who wrote down "just what was said," wrote "knot" instead of "not." In fact, it is only on this assumption that "one too many nots" makes any sense in this context.

There is a "not" in each of the four statements made. Let us draw a diagram, showing what was said.

(Cecilia said "that it was not Belinda or Eve." This is represented on the third line across by putting X's under B and E.)

	A	B	C	D	E
A		X		X	X
B					
C		X			X
D	X		X		
E	X			X	

We have reason to believe that the "not" in 1 of the 4 statements should be crossed out. If it were crossed out in the statements made by Cecilia, Eve, or Anna, there would still be 1 or more X's under all 5. But if the "not" in Dora's statement were crossed out, Dora would have said that it was Anna or Cecilia. It could not be Anna because Belinda said that Eve said that it was not. It could be Cecilia because no one said it was not. $\therefore$ Cecilia was arrested.

Complete Solution

Cecilia was arrested. Dora's statement was wrong.

25. Crimes Assorted

Denote: provoked assault by PA, dangerous drinking by DD, and bobbery by B.

Consider A3. Suppose it is true. Then when asked whether C was a Pukka, B said "yes." Suppose B was telling the truth; then A, B, and C have all made true statements. However, this is not possible (for one of them is a W-W). Suppose B was not telling the truth; then C would not be a Pukka, and B has told a lie. ∴ A must be a Pukka (no one else can be). ∴ A2 is true; ∴ A is not a Pukka. ∴ our original assumption is false; ∴ A3 is false; ∴ A1 is false.

∴ A2 is true; ∴ A is a Sh-Sh. ∴ B2 is false; ∴ B is a W-W, and C is a Pukka.

∴ C3 is true; ∴ A is a DD. and C2 is true; ∴ B is not PA. B1 is false; ∴ A is not a PA. ∴ C did commit PA (by elimination). B(3) is false; ∴ C not B. And C1 is true; ∴ A must be B.

Complete Solution

A is guilty of dangerous drinking and of bobbery.

C is guilty of provoked assault.

26. The Puzzle That Was New

```
                n  -  -  -              (i)
     w  -  )  -  -  -  -  -  -          (ii)
              -  -                      (iii)
              ___
              -  -  n                   (iv)
           e  -  w                      (v)
           _____
              -  w  -                   (vi)
           w  -  -                      (vii)
           _____
                 n                      (viii)
           ======
```

From (iv), (v), and (vi) n must be even ($w + w = n$ or $w + w = 10 + n$). $\therefore$ from n in (i), (iii) must be the divisor $\times 2$ or more. $\therefore$ since (iii) has only 2 figures, w in the divisor must be 4 or less and $n = 2w$. If w were 3, then (iii) would be 3– $\times$ 6 and would have 3 figures. But (iii) only has 2 figures.

By a similar argument, w cannot be 4. If w were 1, then (v) and (vii) cannot be more than 19×9, i.e., 171. But first digits of (v) and (vii) are different (e and w). $\therefore w$ cannot be 1. $\therefore w$ can only be 2. $\therefore n = 4$. If the divisor were 25, then (iii) would have 3 figures ($25 \times 4 = 100$). $\therefore$ second digit in the divisor is less than 5. If the divisor were 23, then (vii) could only be 207 (23×9). But this is not possible, for (viii) would then have 2 figures (and the divisor clearly cannot be less than 23). $\therefore$ the divisor can only be 24. $\therefore$ (iii) is 96 and (vii) is 216 (24×9). $\therefore$ (vi) is 220.

(v) is a multiple of 24 ending in 2. $\therefore$ it must be 24×3 or 24×8. But 24×3 only has 2 figures. $\therefore$ (v) must be 24×8 (i.e., 192). Add up from the bottom (and note that the second figure in (i) is (0), and we get:

Complete Solution

```
              4 0 8 9
      2 4 ) 9 8 1 4 0
            9 6
            ———
              2 1 4
              1 9 2
              ———
                2 2 0
                2 1 6
                ———
                    4
                  ===
```

27. A Disappointed Simple

In (i), n and g (B's and C's games played) cannot be 0 and cannot be more than 3. Since in the second line in (ii) n and g cannot be more than 3, there is nothing to carry, and h in the first line cannot be 0. ∴ in (i), n, g, and h are between them 1, 2, and 3, and y (A's draws) must be 0.

A drew none; ∴ h (A's points) cannot be 1 or 3. ∴ $h = 2$. Since B's games played must be greater than B's games won, n must be 3; ∴ $g = 1$.

C's 1 game must have been against B, who played them all. The score in this game was p–h (which is 2). Since p is greater than 2, C won this game. ∴ B cannot have gotten more than 4 points; ∴ $x = 4$.

B lost against C and won against A and D. But A got 2 points; ∴ they played 2 matches (not 3, for C only played B). ∴ D played 2 matches, to make the total of matches even.

D did not draw a match, for neither A nor B drew one. D had 0 goals for and 3 goals against. ∴ the score in their matches must have been 0–1 and 0–2, but we do not yet know which is which.

Suppose A vs. D was 1–0. Then since A had 4 goals against, A vs. B was ?–4. If p (A's goals for) were 5, A vs. B would be 4–4. But this is not possible, for A only got 2 points. If A's goals for were more than 5, A would get 4 points. ∴ A vs. D must be 2–0 and B vs. D must be 1–0.

If p were 5, A vs. B would be 3–4. But if p were more than 5, A vs. B would be a draw or a win for A. ∴ p can only be 5. ∴ A vs. B was 3–4; C vs. B was 5–2; and t (B's goals for) was 7 (4 + 2 + 1).

Complete Solution

(i)
A vs. B	3–4
A vs. D	2–0
B vs. C	2–5
B vs. D	1–0

(ii) 5 3
    2 1
   ———
   7 4

28. Sergeant Simple in Verse

A's and C's figures (8) are the same. ∴ if one of these figures were wrong, it would not be possible to discover which. ∴ they must both be right. ∴ Either B's figure or D's figure is wrong.

Six matches were played. ∴ 60 points were awarded for wins or draws. A and C could only have gotten 10 of these between them. D can only have gotten 30 of these (even if they won all 3 of their matches). ∴ B must have gotten 20 for wins or draws. But B's figure is only 19. ∴ B's figure is wrong and all the rest are right.

D got 30 points for wins and 27 for goals. ∴ D's score in all 3 matches was 9–1. A's and C's situations must be the same. ∴ they drew against each other and scored 1 goal in each match. ∴ we have:

	A	B	C	D
A		loss 1–?	draw 1–1	loss 1–9
B	win ?–1		win ?–1	loss 1–9
C	draw 1–1	loss 1–?		loss 1–9
D	win 9–1	win 9–1	win 9–1	

We cannot tell the scores in B vs. A and B vs. C, though we know that B won them both. The scores in each case could be anything from 2–1 to 9–1. ∴ B got 20 points for wins and at least 5 points for goals and might have gotten as many as 19 for goals. ∴ B's points are between 25 and 39.

Complete Solution

B's figure was wrong. (It should be between 25 and 39 inclusive.)

A vs. B	1–2 to 9
A vs. C	1–1
A vs. D	1–9
B vs. C	9 to 2–1
B vs. D	1–9
C vs. D	1–9

29. Good Becomes Better

R	R	D	B	T	D	P
R	W	A	D	T	D	P

T	R	W	H	E	M	T	R

(i) (ii) (iii) (iv) (v) (vi) (vii) (viii)

Look first for the incorrect letter. If (viii) is correct, R would have to be even (P + P). But R in (ii) can only be 9 [9 + 9 + 1 (carried) = 19]. ∴ the incorrect letter must be either in (ii) or in (viii). ∴ all the other letters are correct.

In (iii), R must be 0 (0 + W = W) or 9 [9 + W + 1 (carried) = W]. But R cannot be 0, for at least 2 of R's in (ii) would then have to be 0, and neither the first nor the second line can start with 0. ∴ R = 9. In (i), T must be 1. In (iv), D cannot be 0, for there is 1 to carry from (iv) to (iii). ∴ in (vii), D = 5 [5 + 5 + 1 (carried) = 11]. Since there is 1 to carry from (vii), M = 3.

There is not 1 to carry from (vi); ∴ B and E in (v) must differ by 5, the value of D. ∴ one of them must be 2 and the other 7 (there are no other possibilities). If B were 2 and E were 7, there would not be 1 to carry, and A and H in (iv) would have to differ by 5. But this is not possible, for 2 and 7 are the only numbers left that differ by 5. ∴ B = 7 and E = 2. ∴ in (iv), since D = 5, 1 has been carried from (v) and 1 is to be carried to (iii) ∴ A must be 8 and H must be 4. We are left with P and W. One of these must be 0 and the other 6. We know that there is 1 to carry from (viii) ∴ P must be 6. ∴ W = 0. ∴ R in (viii) is the letter that is wrong. It should be 2 (i.e., E).

Complete Solution

R in (viii) is wrong. It should be E.

$$
\begin{array}{c}
9\ 9\ 5\ 7\ 1\ 5\ 6 \\
9\ 0\ 8\ 5\ 1\ 5\ 6 \\
\hline
1\ 9\ 0\ 4\ 2\ 3\ 1\ 2
\end{array}
$$

30. The Vertical Tear

Team	Goals against	Points
A	5	3
B	6	5
C	0	0
D	7	?

Look first for the figure that is wrong. Since each side played at least 1 match, it is not possible for C to have no goals against and get no points. They must at least have drawn 1. ∴ either C's goals against or C's points are wrong. ∴ all the other figures are correct.

Since the incorrect figure is only 1 out, C must either have had 1 goal against and gotten no points or have had no goals against and scored 1 point. Whichever it is, they can only have played 1 match, and the score in this match must have been 0–0 or 0–1.

Since B got 5 points, they must have played all the others and won 2 and drew 1. ∴ C's match was against B. C scored no goals against B. ∴ A and D scored 6 between them, and since A and D either lost or drew these matches, the score in them (from B's point of view) must have been 4–3 or 3–3 (not more than 7 goals in any match).

Since A got 3 points, A must have played D as well as B. Since A cannot have beaten B (for B lost no games), A got 2 points from a win against D and 1 point from a draw against B. ∴ B vs. A was 3–3. ∴ B won their other 2 matches, with results B vs. C 1–0 and B vs. D 4–3.

A had 5 goals against, 3 by B, ∴ 2 by A. D had 7 goals against, 4 by B, ∴ 3 by A.

Complete Solution

A vs. B	3–3
A vs. D	3–2
B vs. C	1–0
B vs. D	4–3

31. The Professor Goes One Better

Points are:

A 22
B 9
C 25
D 8

Only 1 side gets a bonus in each match. In a drawn match either side could get a bonus, but the score must be at least 2–2 (no bonus possible if score is 1–1). It is not possible for the losing side to get a bonus unless the winning side also gets one.

∴ since all sides get bonuses, they must all get points for wins or draws. Since only 4 matches were played, the total of points for wins or draws was 40. No side can win 2 games, for if they did, they would get bonuses in 2 games, but we know that the 4 teams each get a bonus of 1 or more from the 4 matches. ∴ we have:

Team	For wins or draws	For goals and bonuses
A	15	7
B	5	4
C	15	10
D	5	3

D drew 1 match, whose score must have been 2–2, with 1 point for D's bonus. ∴ D only played 1. The 2 matches that were *not* played must have been 2 of D vs. A, D vs. B, D vs. C.

Consider B. A drawn match must have been 2–2 (with 1 point for bonus) and there can only have been 1 other match (lost 1–?). ∴ D vs. B was not played.

Consider A. A drawn match must have been 2–2. Either in this match or in the match that A won we know that A scored 4 goals. Add the bonus of at least 1, and we get 7. But we know that the total of A's goals and bonus is 7. ∴ D vs. A was not played. ∴ all other matches were played, and D's match was against C. ∴ we have:

	A	B	C	D
A		2–2	win	
B	2–2 (bonus of 1)		loss 1–	
C	loss	win –1		2–2
D		2–2 (bonus of 1)		

Consider A vs. C. We know that score was 4–? and that A can only have gotten 1 bonus. ∴ C must have gotten at least 2 goals. (Otherwise we would have an arrangement that produces more than 1 bonus point for A.)

We know that there was a bonus of more than 2 in at least 1 match. But the only match left to consider is C vs. B. ∴ the score in this match was at least 3–1. In this case C has (2 + 3 + 2) goals + 3 bonus points, making 10. And this is correct. ∴ C vs. B was 3–1.

Complete Solution

A vs. B	2–2
A vs. C	4–2
B vs. C	1–3
C vs. D	2–2

32. The Worst Was First

B scored no points for wins or draws and lost 3 matches by a single goal. ∴ the total goals scored by D, A, and C against B was 48 (45 + 3). The total points of D, A, and C was 116 (43 + 39 + 34). Of these 60 were for wins and draws (6 matches played) and 48 were for goals against B. ∴ the total of goals in matches between D, A, and C was 8 (116–60–48).

Since not more than 3 goals were scored in any of these 3 matches and since each match that was won was won by 1 point, the scores in these matches were 2–1, 2–1, and 1–1 (total, 8).

Consider C (34 points). For a win against B, C scored 10 points and at most 4 goals in its other 2 matches. This leaves 34 − 14, i.e., 20. They cannot have gotten more than 18 goals against B; ∴ they must have gotten at least 5 points for wins and draws.

Consider A (39 points). For a win against B, A scored 10 points and at most 4 goals in its other 2 matches. This leaves 39 − 14, i.e., 25. They got not more than 18 goals against B, ∴ at least 10 points for wins or draws.

Consider D (43 points). For a win against B, D scored 10 points and at most 4 goals in its other 2 matches. This leaves 43 − 14, i.e., 29. They got not more than 18 goals against B, ∴ at least 15 points for wins and draws.

There were 3 matches between C, A, and D; ∴ 30 points. ∴ C, A, and D got 5, 10, and 15 for wins and draws. (We know they got at least these figures and none of them can have gotten more without someone else getting less.) ∴ C vs. D was a draw (1–1); D vs. A was 2–1; A vs. C was 2–1. ∴ A vs. B was 16–15 (39 − 10 − 10 − 2 − 1 = 16). ∴ C vs. B was 17–16 (34 − 10 − 5 − 1 − 1 = 17). ∴ D vs. B was 15–14 (43 − 10 − 10 − 5 − 2 − 1 = 15). Finally, B's goals (15 + 16 + 14) add up to 45.

Complete Solution

A vs. B	16–15
A vs. C	2–1
A vs. D	1–2

B vs. C   16–17
B vs. D   14–15
C vs. D   1–1

33. Not Far Enough

```
              2 5 3 - -                    (i)
      3 9 ) - - - - - -                    (ii)
          4 7                              (iii)
          ———
          2 - -                            (iv)
          1 8 0                            (v)
          ———
            5 - -                          (vi)
            3 2 6                          (vii)
            ———
              9 -                          (viii)
              5 1                          (ix)
              ———
              1 6 2                        (x)
            - 4 4                          (xi)
              ═══
```

(The reader is advised to have a figure like the following in which to fill in the correct figures as they are discovered.)

```
              - - - - -
      - - ) - - - - - -
          - -
          ———
          - - -
          - - -
          ———
            - - -
            - - -
            ———
              - -
              - -
              ═══
              - - -
              - - -
              ═══
```

The divisor cannot start with 1, for $19 \times 9 = 171$. ∴ all 3-figure multiples of 1 – start with 1, and 1 is the figure given in (v). ∴ the first figure of (v) is at least 2, and the first figure of (iv) is at least 3

123

(2 is the figure given); ∴ the divisor cannot start with 2, nor can it start with 3 (figure given). ∴ it starts with 4 or more. ∴ it cannot go 3 times into the first 2 figures of (ii), and it does not go twice (2 is figure given). ∴ the first figure in (i) is 1.

(iii) does not start with 4 (the figure given). ∴ it starts with 5 or more. ∴ (ix) is the same as the divisor. ∴ the divisor does not start with 5 [the figure given in (ix)]. ∴ the first figure in the divisor [and in (iii)] is 6 or more. Since the first figure in (iv) is 3 or more, ∴ the first figure in the divisor [and in (iii)] must be 6, the first figure in (ii) is 9, the first figure in (iv) is 3, and the first figure in (ix) is 6.

The divisor cannot end in 0, for in that case all multiples of it would end in 0, and (v) does not (figure given). The divisor does not end in 9 (figure given), nor in 7 [figure given in (iii)], nor in 1 [figure given in (ix)]. (viii) does not start with 9 (figure given), but with 8 or less. ∴ (x) starts with 2 or 1. Since 1 is the figure given, it must start with 2.

If the divisor were 65, then (x) and (xi) would be 260 (no other possibility); but they are not [see the second figure of (x)]. ∴ the divisor is not 65. If the divisor were 63, then (x) and (xi) would be 252, but they are not; ∴ it is not 63. If the divisor were 62, then (x) and (xi) would be 248, but they are not; ∴ it is not 62. If the divisor were 66, then (x) and (xi) would be 264, but they are not; ∴ it is not 66. If the divisor were 68, then (x) and (xi) would be 272 (68 × 4) or 204 (68 × 3). But (x) and (xi) do not end in 2 or 4; ∴ it is not 68. ∴ the divisor must be 64.*

(v) must start with 2 or 3. ∴ it is 64 × 4, 5, or 6. But not 5 [see (i)] and not 6 [384]; ∴ it is 64 × 4 (256). Since (x) starts with 2, (x) and (xi) must be 256. The difference between (vi) and (vii) is less than 10. Since (vii) is not 192 (64 × 3) [3 is the figure given in (i)], (vi) and (vii) must start with same number. It cannot be 3 or 5 (figure given). ∴ it must be 1, 2, or 4. But not 192 (see above), not 128 (64 × 2) [2 is figure given in (vii)], and not 256 (64 × 4) (6 is figure given). ∴ (vii) must be 448.

Add up from the bottom, and we get:

Complete Solution

```
                   1 4 7 1 4
         6 4 ) 9 4 1 6 9 6
               6 4
               ─────
               3 0 1
               2 5 6
               ─────
                   4 5 6
                   4 4 8
                   ─────
                       8 9
                       6 4
                       ─────
                       2 5 6
                       2 5 6
                       ═════
```

* It will be convenient to put down the multiples of 64, thus:

$$64 \times 1 = 64$$
$$\times 2 = 128$$
$$\times 3 = 192$$
$$\times 4 = 256$$
$$\times 5 = 320$$
$$\times 6 = 384$$
$$\times 7 = 448$$
$$\times 8 = 512$$
$$\times 9 = 576$$

34. The Last Croak of Doctor Dope

To get to Criss Cross from W (4 mi) by bicycle takes 16 min.
To get to Criss Cross from X (5 mi) by bicycle takes 20 min.
To get to Criss Cross from Y (5 mi) by bicycle takes 20 min.
To get to Criss Cross from Z (7 mi) by bicycle takes 28 min.

Consider Quick's movements. Quick missed the 10:09 train from Y; ∴ he must have bicycled and could not have arrived before 10:32. If he then bicycled on, he would not have arrived at X until 10:52, but we know he was in X at 10:47. ∴ he took the train and left Criss Cross at 10:33. ∴ he was only in Criss Cross from 10:32 to 10:33. ∴ Quick is not guilty.

Consider Racy. Suppose Racy bicycled to Criss Cross. Then he could not have arrived before 10:30 and would therefore have missed the train to Z. If he bicycled on, he would not have arrived in Z until 10:58, but we know he was there at 10:55. ∴ Racy did not bicycle to Criss Cross. ∴ Racy must have caught the 10:11 train and arrived at Criss Cross at 10:26. He therefore just missed the 10:25 train from Criss Cross to Z and must have gone on by bicycle. This would have taken him 28 min, so if he got on his bicycle straightaway, he would have gotten to Z at 10:54. ∴ He can only have been 1 min at Criss Cross (from 10:26 to 10:27) and is therefore not guilty.

Consider Sleepy. Sleepy was in W at 10:13 and therefore missed the 10:11 train. If he bicycled to Criss Cross, he could have arrived at 10:29. He then would have missed the train to Y (which left at 10:25) and therefore must have bicycled on. This would have taken him 20 min, and he need not therefore have left Criss Cross until 10:32. Sleepy could therefore have been in Criss Cross from 10:32 and could be guilty.

Consider Dozy. Suppose Dozy bicycled to Criss Cross. He could then have arrived at 10:30 and therefore missed the train to W. If he bicycled straight on, he would have arrived in W at 10:46, but we know that he was in W at 10:45. ∴ Dozy must have caught the 10:03 train and arrived in Criss Cross at 10:22. The train to W would not get him there until 10:49. ∴ he must have bicycled on. This would have taken him 16 min, so he need not have left Criss Cross until 10:29, which is 16 min earlier than

126

10:45. He could therefore have had 7 min in Criss Cross, but as he must have left at 10:29 and the doctor was seen alive at 10:28, he did not have time to murder him.

Complete Solution

Sleepy was the murderer.

35. The Multiplication That Was Worse Than Vexation

```
T  M  B  T  P  M  G        (i)
                  T        (ii)
─────────────────────
G  E  D  E  E  X  T  G      (iii)
```

Let us consider the possible values of G, the last letter in (i) and the first and last letter in (iii). There are various possibilities if G is 5, but suppose, first, that G is not 5.

If T were 6 and G were 2 ($6 \times 2 = 12$), we would have 3 at the beginning of (iii) ($6 \times 6 = 36$). But if G were 2, we should have 2. If T were 6 and G were 4 ($6 \times 4 = 24$), there would be 2 to carry from the last line down. And M, the last figure but one in (i), would have to be *either* 4 ($6 \times 4 = 24$, and 2 makes 26) *or* 9 ($6 \times 9 = 54$, and 2 makes 56). But M cannot be 4, for we are assuming that G is 4.

If M were 9, there would be 5 to carry to the second digit of (iii) ($6 \times 9 = 54$), and (iii) would start 41 ($6 \times 6 = 36$, and 5 makes 41). ∴ E would be 1. Since $6 \times 6 = 36$, and the fifth letter of (iii) is 1, 4 must be carried to the fourth letter of (iii).

But whatever B is, $6 \times B$ is even, and when 4 is added, it is still even. But we are assuming that E is 1. ∴ this is not possible. ∴ M cannot be 9. ∴ G cannot be 4 if T is 6. If T were 6 and G were 8, we would have $6 \times 8 = 48$. We would then have at the beginning of (i) 6×6, i.e., 36. But it would not then be possible for the first G in (iii) to be 8.

We have now considered all the possibilities if G is not 5. ∴ G must be 5. T in (ii) must be odd. ($5 \times 3 = 15$, $5 \times 4 = 20$). But T is not 1 and not 3, for the first figure in (iii) could not then be 5. And T is not 5, for G is 5, and not 9, since the first figure in (iii), G, would then be 8. ∴ T can only be 7.

From the last line down 3 is carried ($7 \times 5 = 35$). ∴ we have $7 \times M + 3 = 7$ or 17 or 27, etc. ∴ $7 \times M = 4$ or 14 or 24, etc. The only possibility here is for M to be 2 ($7 \times 2 + 3 = 17$).

Consider the first digit of (i), 7. $7 \times 7 = 49$, so that there is at least 1 to carry from 7×2. But there cannot be more than 2. ∴ E

128

must be 0 or 1. Suppose that E is 0. Then the fifth digit of (iii) would be 0, so that there would be only 1 to carry from $7 \times P$. $\therefore$ P would have to be 1 or 2. But not 2, for M is 2. And if P were 1, there would be nothing to carry. $\therefore$ E cannot be 0, $\therefore$ E is 1. $\therefore$ 2 is carried from $7 \times P$. If P were 3 (it cannot be 1 or 2), we would have $7 \times P + 1 = 22$. But M is 2. If P were 4, we would have $7 \times P + 1 = 29$, and X would be 9. And since only 2 is carried, this must be correct. $\therefore P = 4$, $X = 9$.

Consider B, the third letter in (i). We know that $7 \times B + 5 = -1$. $\therefore$ we want a multiple of 7 that ends in 6 ($6 + 5 = 11$). This can only be 7×8 (i.e., 56) $\therefore B = 8$ $\therefore$ D in (iii) is 0 ($7 \times 2 + 6 = 20$).

Complete Solution

$$
\begin{array}{r}
7\ 2\ 8\ 7\ 4\ 2\ 5 \\
7 \\
\hline
5\ 1\ 0\ 1\ 1\ 9\ 7\ 5 \\
\hline
\end{array}
$$

36. "Four Tribes Are Better Than Three"

The only way in which the truth-telling rules of the Jokers can be different from those of the other 3 tribes is for their first and third statements to have different truth-values; i.e., one must be false and the other true. The second statement could be true or false.

Suppose C2 was true. Then B is a Pukka. ∴ D is a Sh-Sh. ∴ A would have to be a W-W. But A1 could not then be false. ∴ C2 cannot be true.

Suppose C3 is false. Then C1 would also be false, and C would be a W-W, and neither D nor B nor C could be a Pukka. ∴ A would have to be a Pukka. ∴ A1 would be true, but if C3 were false, A1 could not be true. ∴ C3 cannot be false, ∴ C is a Joker and C1 is false. Since neither B nor D is a Pukka, A must be a Pukka. If B1 were true, D would be a Sh-Sh and B would be a W-W, but B2 could not then be true. ∴ B1 is false. ∴ B must be a Sh-Sh. ∴ D must be a W-W.

Complete Solution

A is a Pukka.
B is a Shilli-Shalla.
C is a Joker.
D is a Wotta-Woppa.

37. Addition: Letters for Digits (Two Numbers)

K	R	A	M	Y	R
K	Q	E	M	Y	R

Y	A	H	E	K	Y

(i) (ii) (iii) (iv) (v) (vi)

From (vi), Y must be even (R + R). ∴ Y is 2, 4, 6, or 8 [not 0, for Y in (i) cannot be 0].

K in (i) must be 1, 2, 3, or 4 (not more, for if K were 5 or more, there would be another figure in the bottom line). If K in (i) were 1, then Y would be 2, and R in (vi) would be 6 (6 + 6 = 12). If K in (i) were 2, then Y would be 4 and R in (vi) would be 7 (7 + 7 = 14), and so on. In every case there must be 1 to carry from (vi) to (v). ∴ K must be odd (Y + Y + 1). ∴ K = 1 or 3, but not 1, for Y would then be 2 and K in (v) would be 5. ∴ K = 3. ∴ Y = 6 and R in (vi) is 8.

Since there is not 1 to carry from (ii) to (i), A must be 9 and Q is then 0 or 1. Since A in (iii) is 9, there must be 1 to carry from (iii); ∴ Q = 0. In (iii), since A = 9, there cannot be 1 to carry from (iv), for if there were, E and H would be the same. ∴ E − H = 1. Since from (iv), E is odd (M + M + 1), E must be 5 and H must be 4 (the only 2 consecutive numbers left such that the bigger one is odd). ∴ in (iv), M = 2.

Complete Solution

3	8	9	2	6	8
3	0	5	2	6	8

6	9	4	5	3	6

38. Addition: Letters for Digits (Four Numbers)

K	B	R	A	K	P
P	H	R	E	P	K
K	M	R	D	X	P
K	B	R	E	K	X

H	P	H	D	E	E

(i)   (ii)   (iii)   (iv)   (v)   (vi)

Consider (v) and (vi). In (vi), P + K + P + X = E (or E + 10, 20, or 30). In (v), K + P + X + K = E (or E + 10, 20, or 30) + 1, 2, or 3 [carried from (vi)]. ∴ P + K + P + X > K + P + X + K by 1, 2, or 3. ∴ P > K by 1, 2, or 3 [i.e., by the number carried from (vi) to (v)].

Consider (i). We know that P is not greater than K by more than 3. Suppose it is 3. Then K would be 1 and P would be 4 [2 and 5 would not be possible, for H in (i) would then be more than 9]. (vi) would be 4 + 1 + 4 + (at most) 9, i.e., 18. In this case only 1 is carried from (vi) ∴ P − K can only be 1. If K were 2 and P were 3, then (i) would be 2 + 3 + 2 + 2, i.e., 9, which would be all right if nothing were carried from (ii). But H in (ii) would then be 9. ∴ there would be something to carry from (ii). ∴ K can only be 1 and P can only be 2.

We know that there is 1 to carry from (vi) to (v). ∴ X must be 5, 8, or 9; E must be 0, 3, or 4. [X and E must differ by 5, i.e., 10 − (2 + 1 + 2)]. E cannot be 1 for K is 1, or 2 for P is 2). There is 1 to carry from (v) to (iv). ∴ A = E + D + E + 1 = D + 10, 20, or 30. E must be 0, 3, or 4. If E were 4, then A + 4 + 4 + 1 = 10, 20, or 30. ∴ A could only be 1. But K = 1. If E were 3, then A + 3 + 3 + 1 = 10, 20, or 30. ∴ A could only be 3, but we are assuming that E is 3. ∴ E must be 0 (A + 0 + 0 + 1 = 10, 20, or 30). ∴ X = 5 and A = 9. There is 1 to carry from (iv) to (iii); ∴ H must be odd (for R + R + R + R is even). H in (i) must be at least 6 (see above), but since it must be odd, it can only be 7. ∴ H = 7. ∴ R in (iii) can only be 4 or 9 (4 + 4 + 4 + 4 + 1 = 17; 9 + 9 + 9 + 9 = 37). But A = 9; ∴ R = 4 [and there is 1 to carry from (iii) to (ii)]. The digits left are 3, 6, and 8, and they must be between them B,

132

D, and M. Since H is 7, 2 is carried from (ii) to (i); ∴ in (ii) we have B + 7 + M + B + 1 = 22. If B were 8, then the left-hand side would be more than 22. If B were 6, then we would have 6 + 7 + M + 6 + 1 = 22 and M would have to be 2. But this is not possible since P is 2. ∴ B must be 3, and we have 3 + 7 + M + 3 + 1 = 22. ∴ M must be 8. ∴ D must be 6.

Complete Solution

```
1 3 4 9 1 2
2 7 4 0 2 1
1 8 4 6 5 2
1 3 4 0 1 5
───────────
7 2 7 6 0 0
═══════════
```

39. Addition: Letters for Digits (Four of Them Missing)

	G	T	K	T	G	P	K	M	
–		K	–	D	–	P	–	M	(x)

M	G	M	P	K	P	M	N	T

(i) (ii) (iii) (iv) (v) (vi) (vii) (viii) (ix)

There are 6 letters (D, G, K, M, P, and T), and since all digits are included, the 4 blank spaces must be filled with 4 different digits that do not appear elsewhere. M in (i) can only be 1. Also, the first figure in (x) must be 9 and there must be 1 to carry from (iii) (G + 9 + 1 = 10 + G). We cannot yet say what G is.

In (ix), T = 2 (M + M). In (iii), K = 8 [not 9, for the first digit in (x) is 9], and there must be 1 to carry from (iv). ∴ in (viii), we have 8 + 3 = 11.

In (vii) P must be 0 or 5 (0 + 0 + 1 = 1; 5 + 5 + 1 = 11). But if P were 0, then in (iv) we would have 8 + 1 or 2 = 10 which is impossible since the blank spaces must be filled with digits that do not appear elsewhere. ∴ P = 5, and there is 1 to carry from (vii) to (vi).

In (v), since T = 2 and K = 8, there cannot be 1 to carry to (iv). ∴ in (iv), we have 8 + 7 = 15. ∴ in (v), D must be 6 (not 5 since P = 5).

The only digits left are 0 and 4. ∴ G must be 4 (not 0, for we cannot have 0 at the beginning of a line). ∴ (vi) is 4 + 0 + 1 (carried) = 5.

Complete Solution

```
    4 2 8 2 4 5 8 1
    9 8 7 6 0 5 3 1
  ─────────────────
  1 4 1 5 8 5 1 1 2
  ═════════════════
```

40. Multiplication: Letters for Digits

```
Y M G Y B M P          (i)
              P        (ii)
_____
P A X H E B Y          (iii)
```

P in (ii) must be 2 or more. ∴ P, at the beginning of (iii), must be more than Y at the beginning of (i). Y must be less than 5 (for 5 × 2 = 10). ∴ Y = 1, 2, 3, or 4. But P × P ends with Y. Since a perfect square cannot end in 2 or 3, Y must be 1 or 4.

If Y were 4, P would be 2 or 8 (2 × 2 = 4; 8 × 8 = 64). But P cannot be 2, for P must be more than Y. If P were 8, then since 8 × 4 = 32, there would be another figure in (iii). Y can only be 1, and since P cannot also be 1, P must be 9 (9 × 9 = 81).

Since 9 × 1 = 9, there is nothing to carry to the first digit of (iii). ∴ M must be 0. ∴ B [the last digit but one in (iii)] must be 8 (9 × 9 = 81). ∴ E = 2 (9 × 8 = 72). ∴ H = 6 (9 × 1 + 7 = 16).

The letters left are G, A, and X and the digits left are 3, 4, 5, and 7. Suppose G were 3. Then X would be 7 + 1, i.e., 8 (9 × 3 = 27). But B = 8. Suppose G were 5. Then X would be 5 + 1, i.e., 6 (9 × 5 = 45). But H = 6. Suppose G were 7. Then X would be 3 + 1, i.e., 4 (9 × 7 = 63). And A would then be 6. But H = 6. ∴ G can only be 4. ∴ X is 6 + 1, i.e., 7 (9 × 4 = 36). And A = 3.

Complete Solution

```
1 0 4 1 8 0 9
            9
_____
9 3 7 6 2 8 1
```

41. Old Method (Four Teams)

Consider C. They got no points; ∴ they could not have won or drawn a match. But they can only have lost 1, for goals against (3) are only 1 greater than goals for (2). Since D got 5 points, they played all the other 3. ∴ C vs. D was 2–3, and C did not play A or B.

A got 3 points; they did not play C. ∴ they played B and D. ∴ they must have drawn against D (who lost none), and they must have won against B. Since D drew against A, they won against B. ∴ B lost both its matches. Since they only had 2 goals against, the score in each match was 0–1. ∴ B vs. A was 0–1, and B vs. D was 0–1. A had 4 goals against, none by B, ∴ 4 by D. ∴ A vs. D was 4–4.

Complete Solution

A vs. B	1–0
A vs. D	4–4
B vs. D	0–1
C vs. D	2–3

42. Bungle Blunders Yet Again

Look first for the figure that is wrong. We are told that C played 2 games; ∴ they played A and B. But if A played C, they must, between them, have gotten at least 2 points. But we are told that they only got 1 point. ∴ either C's games played or A's points (1) or C's points (0) must be wrong. ∴ all other figures are correct.

B scored 5 goals for; but A and C between them only had 5 goals against (2 + 3). ∴ B must have played A and C, and B vs. A must have been 2–? and B vs. C must have been 3–?. If A played C, the score was ?–0 (for A had 2 goals against by B, ∴ none by C); and C had 3 goals against by B, ∴ none by A. ∴ if A played C, the score was 0–0. ∴ A vs. B was 2–2. ∴ A would have 2 points, and C would have 1 point for a drawn match against A. But this would make 2 of the figures wrong (A's points and C's points). ∴ A cannot have played C, and the figure wrong is C's games played; it should be 1 not 2.

Complete Solution

C's games played was wrong; it should be 1 not 2.

A vs. B   2–2
B vs. C   3–1

43. More Goals and More Attractive Soccer

All of B's points must have been gotten through goals. ∴ B lost both its matches. A, with 20 points, must have scored at least 5 goals; and C, with 19 points, must have scored at least 4. In fact, since the total number of points awarded for 3 matches is 30, they cannot have scored more than this.∴ A got 15 points from wins and draws, B got none, and C got 15. ∴ A must have drawn with C, and A and C both beat B.

Suppose A vs. C was 2-2. Then A scored 3 goals against B and C scored 2 goals against B. B was beaten by both A and C and therefore could not have scored more than 2 goals against A, and 1 goal against C. But B scored 5 goals altogether. ∴ A vs. C cannot have been 2-2. (The reader might like to check that A vs. C could not have been 3-3.) ∴ A vs. C must have been 1-1. ∴ A scored 4 goals against B, and C scored 3 goals against B. Since B lost both its matches and scored 5 goals altogether, they must have scored 3 against A and 2 against C.

Complete Solution

A vs. B	4-3
A vs. C	1-1
B vs. C	2-3

44. Uncle Bungle's New Soccer Puzzle (Letters for Digits)

Since the 4 teams are going to play each other once, no team can have played more than 3 games.

In C's line the letters p, x, h, and k must all be different and p must be bigger than the others. $\therefore p = 3$, and x, h, and k must be 0, 1, and 2, but we do not yet know which is which. A and D played at least 1 match (for C played them all). $\therefore x$ and k cannot be 0; $\therefore h$ must be 0. A played x and drew k; $\therefore x$ must be greater than k. $\therefore x = 2$ and $k = 1$. $\therefore$ C got 5 points (2 wins and 1 draw). $\therefore m = 5$. Since the total of matches played must be even, B must have played 2.

D only played 1 game, $\therefore$ it was against C. D vs. A and D vs. B were the only 2 matches that were not played.

B won none and had 5 goals for and 5 against. $\therefore$ they drew both their matches against A and against C. $\therefore$ A scored no goals but had 3 goals against. $\therefore$ A vs. B was 0–0 and A vs. C was 0–3. Since B vs. A was 0–0, B vs. C was 5–5.

C had t goals for and we know that C won their match against D. $\therefore$ the score in C vs. D can only be 1–0, for t cannot be more than 9 ($3 + 5 + 1 = 9$).

Complete Solution

A vs. B	0–0
A vs. C	0–3
B vs. C	5–5
C vs. D	1–0

45. Letters for Digits (Five Teams)

No team can play more than 4 games. $\therefore x, m, h, r,$ and p must be 0, 1, 2, 3, and 4, but we do not yet know which is which.

$x, h,$ and r cannot be 0 since A, C, and D had goals for or against; m cannot be 0, for since g must be at least 5, B must have won at least 1. $\therefore p$ must be 0.

From A's matches we know x must be greater than h. Suppose that h were 2. Then x would be 4. But if h were 2, C and D would both have drawn matches against A. Since B drew none, m must be at least 3, and r would be the only letter that could be 1. But if r were 1 and h were 2, D's only match, against A, would be a draw. But this is not possible for D's goals for and against are not the same. $\therefore h$ cannot be 2 and can only be 1. And A's drawn match must have been against D.

$\therefore$ D points must be odd; r can only be 3. Since A scored no goals, they cannot have won a match. $\therefore x = 2. \therefore m$ must be 4. $\therefore$ B got 8 points. $\therefore g = 8$. A did not score a goal and had 3 goals against. $\therefore$ A vs. D was 0–0. A's other match (against B, who played them all) was 0–3. C's 1 match was against B, and the score was 2–4. Since t (B's goals for) cannot be more than 9, B vs. D and B vs. E were both 1–0.

We know that D played 3; $\therefore$ D played E. Since D got 3 points, they won this match. E scored 4 goals (m) and 8 goals against (g). $\therefore$ since E vs. B was 0–1, E vs. D was 4–7. Since D had $(0 + 0 + 7)$ goals for, $y = 7$. And D had $(0 + 1 + 4)$ goals against, $\therefore k = 5$.

Complete Solution

A vs. B	0–3
A vs. D	0–0
B vs. C	4–2
B vs. D	1–0
B vs. E	1–0
D vs. E	7–4

46. Soccer and Addition: Letters for Digits

No one can play more than 3 matches. ∴ *j, x,* and *m* must be 1, 2, and 3 though we do not yet know which is which. From (ii), *m must be 3.*

B, C, and D between them have played 6 matches (1 + 2 + 3). A must have played 2 to make the total even. If *x* (A's drawn matches) stood for 2, then A would have drawn both the matches they played. But this is not possible (see A's goals for and against). ∴ *x must be 1* and *j must be 2.* ∴ since *x* is 1, C only played 1 match, which must have been against D. ∴ *C vs. D was 2–3.*

Since in (ii), *k, p,* and *h* cannot be 3 or less (it would not make sense for any of them to be 0) and since 4 + 5 = 9, *h must be 9* and *k* and *p* must be 4 and 5 though we do not yet know which is which.

No team can get more than 6 points. All digits (except 0) up to 5 are accounted for, and D's points cannot be 0 for we know that D beat C. ∴ *t can only be 6,* and D won all its matches. ∴ A's drawn match can only have been against B.

Suppose B vs. A was 1–1. Then, since B had 3 goals for and 6 goals against, B vs. D would be 2–5 and A vs. D would be 2–3 or 4. D's matches would then be 3 or 4–2, 5–2, and 3–2, and D would then have 11 or 12 goals for instead of 9. It is easy to see that if A vs. B was 0–0, the situation would be worse.

Suppose A vs. B was 3–3. Then D vs. B would be 3–0, D vs. A would be 1 or 2–0, and D vs. C would be 3–2. D would now have 7 or 8 goals for instead of 9. ∴ A vs. B can only be 2–2; B vs. D must be 1–4; since D had 9 goals for, D vs. A must be 2–1; and *k* stands for 4 and *p* for 5.

Complete Solution

(i) A vs. B   2–2
A vs. D   1–2
B vs. D   1–4
C vs. D   2–3

(ii) 4 1
5 2
———
9 3
═══

47. A Cross Number (3 by 3)

Consider 2 down and 4 across. The first digit of 4 across has got to be the same as the second digit of 2 down, which equals 4 across × 3. 4 across, the sum of whose digits is 8, can only be 17, 26, 35, 44, 53, 62, or 71.

It is not 17 or 26, for 3 × 26 is only 78; not 35, for 2 down would then be 105, and the second digit is not 3; not 44, for 2 down would then be 132, and the second digit is not 4; not 62, for 2 down would then be 186, and the second digit is not 6; and not 71, for 2 down would then be 213, and the second digit is not 7. But if 4 across were 53, then 2 down would be 159, which is all right. ∴ 4 across is 53 and 2 down is 159.

Consider 3 down and 5 across. Since 1 across is odd, 3 down must be 135. 5 across reversed is 59–. To be divisible by 6 it must be even, and the sum of its digits must be divisible by 3. ∴ it must be 594 reversed. 5 across is then 495.

The sum of the digits of 5 across is 18. ∴ the sum of the digits of 1 across is 9. ∴ 1 across is 711.

Complete Solution

¹7	²1	³1
■	⁴5	3
⁵4	9	5

143

48. A Cross Number (5 by 5)

Consider 8 across and 8 down. 8 across must be 23, 46, 69, or 92. 8 down must be 19, 38, 57, 76, or 95. ∴ 8 across can only be 92, and 8 down can only be 95.

∴ 10 across must be 56789. 7 down, ending in 9, must be 169, 289, 529, or 729. But the first figure of 7 down is the third figure of 6 across (a perfect cube), which can only be 125. ∴ 7 down is 529.

The first digit of 4 down must be 1, and the last digit must be 9. 9 across can only be 32 (23 is a prime number).

The first 2 digits of 12 across add up to 3. 11 down is a prime number; ∴ it must be 71. And 2 down is 26262.

Consider 5 across. The square root of 7 down is 23; ∴ 5 across must be 46.

Consider 1 across, 1 down, and 3 down. 1 across must be 5281; 1 down must be 54; and 3 down 81.

Complete Solution

^{1}5	^{2}2	^{3}8	^{4}1	■
^{5}4	6	^{6}1	2	^{7}5
^{8}9	2	■	^{9}3	2
^{10}5	6	^{11}7	8	9
■	^{12}2	1	9	■

49. Ages and Shacks on the Island

Suppose C1 is true. Then A2 is true and D would have to be a Pukka. A, C, and D would all make true statements; ∴ B would have to be a W-W. Therefore, C3 must be false. But if C1 is true, C3 should also be true. ∴ our assumption was wrong and C1 is not true.

∴ A2 is not true and C3 is not true. Since A2 is false, D does not belong to a more truthful tribe than A. ∴ A, C, and D all make false statements. ∴ B must be a Pukka. ∴ A1 is true and A3 is true. We know that D3 is true (see A's and C's statements); ∴ D1 is true.

Consider A2. If D does not belong to a more truthful tribe than A, then D2 must be false and A and D belong to the same tribe (Sh-Sh). ∴ C2 must be false, for we know that C must be a W-W.

We now know the tribes to which each of them belongs and which of their statements are true and which are false. We know that the number of B's shack is greater than that of anybody else and that C's number is less than that of anybody else. C's age is greater than that of anybody else, and B's age is less. A and D live in the same shack, and their ages are also the same.

From B1 (true), we know that if D's shack is y, then A's age is $y - 15$. From B3 (true), we know "someone's shack" is $y - 15 - 24$; it can only be C's. And since C2 is false, someone does live in number 1. This can only be C. ∴ $y - 15 - 24 = 1$, ∴ $y = 40$. ∴ A's and D's shack's number is 40, and their ages are 25.

From D1 (true), B's age is $17 + 1$, i.e., 18. ∴ from A3 (true), C's age is $49 + 18$, i.e., 67. From B2 (true), $67 + 18$ is the number of someone's shack. ∴ B's shack must be 85.

Complete Solution

A is a Shilli-Shalla aged 25, and his shack is 40.
B is a Pukka aged 18, and his shack is 85.
C is a Wotta-Woppa aged 67, and his shack is 1.
D is a Shilli-Shalla aged 25, and his shack is 40.

50. Some Island Soccer

Suppose A2 is false. Then B is a W-W. ∴ C would be Pukka (the other 2 have both made false statements), and A would be a Sh-Sh. Consider A1 and C1 (both true on our assumption). From A1: Pukkas (C) beat W-W's (B). From C1: B beat C. But these cannot both be true. ∴ our assumption is false. ∴ A2 is true.

∴ B is not a W-W. ∴ C is a W-W (A has made a true statement).

Consider B1 and B3. If B were a Pukka, both statements would be true. ∴ B (Pukka) would have scored altogether 3 goals (1 + 2). But we know from C2 (false) that B did not score 3 goals. ∴ B is not a Pukka. ∴ A is a Pukka, and B is a Sh-Sh.

B3 states that the score in A vs. B was 2–0, but B1 states that it was 3–1. ∴ these are both false, and B2 is true.

From A3 (true) we know C scored no goals against B. But we know that C was not beaten by B (C1 false). ∴ C vs. B was 0–0.

Consider C3 (false). We know that C scored no goals against B. ∴ C scored at least 1 against A. A vs. C was won by A (A1 true). ∴ the score was at least 2–1.

Consider B2 (true). A vs. B was not 3–1 or 2–0 (B1 and B3 are false). ∴ at least 2 goals were scored by B. ∴ since only 5 goals were scored in A's matches, A vs. C was 2–1 and A vs. B was 0–2.

Complete Solution

Alf is a Pukka.
Bert is a Shilli-Shalla.
Charlie is a Wotta-Woppa.

A vs. B	0–2
A vs. C	2–1
B vs. C	0–0

51. Hopes and Successes

We are told that the truth-telling rules of the Jokers are differ-ent from those of the other 3 tribes. The only way in which this can happen is for the Joker's first and third statement to have different truth values. i.e., one must be false and the other must be true. The second one could be false or true.

Suppose that C3 is true. Then B is a Pukka. ∴ B2 is true and D2 is true. ∴ B, C, and D have all made true remarks. ∴ A should be a W-W. But if C3 is true, the A1 would be true since B would be a Pukka. ∴ our assumption is false and C3 cannot be true.

If C1 were true, then D would be the Joker. But if C1 were true, C would be the Joker (C1 true and C3 false). ∴ C1 cannot be true.

∴ D is not the Joker and either A or B must be the Joker. Since C is not the Joker, D3 is true. ∴ D1 is true (D is not the Joker). ∴ B is the Joker.

Suppose that B2 were false. Then D2 would be false. ∴ A would have to be the Pukka. ∴ A1 would be true and B would make more true statements than D. But if A were the Pukka, B could not make more than 2 true statements, and we know that D makes 2. ∴ A1 cannot be true. ∴ A cannot be a Pukka. And since B is a Joker, D must be a Pukka (no one else can be). ∴ D2 is true. ∴ B2 is true. Since A1 is false, A3 is false. ∴ C is not a W-W. ∴ C must be a Sh-Sh and A must be a W-W.

From C2 (true), we know C's income is 10 Successes. From D2 (true), D's income is 9 Successes (we know that D's income is less than C's). Since C makes 1 true statement, D makes 3 and B makes 2. ∴ B's income can only be 9.50 Successes. We know that B3 is false. ∴ B1 is true. ∴ A's income is 12.00 Successes.

Complete Solution

A is a Wotta-Woppa; his income is 12.00 Successes.
B is a Joker; his income is 9.50 Successes.
C is a Shilli-Shalla; his income is 10.00 Successes.
D is a Pukka; his income is 9 Successes.